Bossart
America's Forgotten Rocket Scientist

Photograph by J.R. Eyeman for Life Magazine, Curtesy of Getty Images

Bossart
America's Forgotten Rocket Scientist

Don P. Mitchell

Bossart: America's Forgotten Rocket Scientist

This book was typeset in Garamond, a font designed by Claud Garamond and first used in 1530. Titles use the modern Segoi UI sans serif font, designed by Steve Matteson in 2004. Composition and layout were done in Word 2010.

Some photographs were repaired and panoramas assembled from movie frames using Adobe Photoshop, Microsoft Image Composite Editor (ICE). Some Flemish and Afrikaans sources were scanned or translated with the aid of the ABBYY FineReader optical character recognition program and the SYSTRAN natural-language software.

Printed in the United States of America.

Contents

Introduction

In the summer of 1957, the Soviet Union and the United States were testing the most powerful weapon ever devised: the intercontinental ballistic missile. It was a rocket capable of carrying a hydrogen bomb halfway around the world. Reaching hypersonic speed, an ICBM would travel too swiftly to be intercepted by any existing defense system as it arced through space and dropped from the sky over its target.

Western experts did not believe the Soviet Union had the technology to build long-range rockets. But the Russians had worked steadily and secretly, since the end of World War II, developing a series of increasingly powerful missiles. By the summer of 1957, at a secret base in Kazakhstan, they were ready to launch the R-7, the biggest rocket ever built.

In America, work on an ICBM had started shortly after the war, but the Air Force vacillated and then cancelled the project before much progress could be made. The very concept of an intercontinental missile was ridiculed as science fiction. Certainly at that time, no rocket was powerful enough to fly thousands of miles, and existing gyroscopes were not accurate enough to hit a target even as big as a city. Some researchers were confident that these problems could be solved, but one famous and influential MIT professor assured Congress that such advances in propulsion and guidance systems were technical impossibilities. However, in the early 1950s, intelligence reports began to reveal the extent of Russia's progress in rocketry. Alarmed by these developments, the Air Force embarked on a crash program to build an intercontinental missile, with only a few years to catch up.

The strategic implications of the ICBM were profound. Since anti-aircraft defenses were useless against it, the only protection against a devastating thermonuclear barrage was the threat of an equally devastating retaliation. Governments began to use the mathematics of game theory to work out the optimal policies, and terms like "first strike" and "mutually assured destruction" entered the vocabulary. Once the two nations embarked on the development of these rockets, neither could afford to fail and be left without a counter threat. If only one side had ICBMs, it would dangerously upset the balance of power.

There were few places the U.S. could turn for rapid development of a long-range missile. The most famous rocket designer of the time was Wernher von Braun. The former Nazi weapons designer was a household name from his popular writings and televised speeches about space exploration, but he and his team of captured German engineers were working on short-range missiles for the Army. His Redstone rocket was only an upgrade of the V-2. With a range of just a few hundred miles, it was far from the capability of an ICBM.

The Navy's rocket program was led by Milton Rosen, who was focused on high-altitude scientific research. He would soon become famous for the notorious Vanguard rocket, which collapsed and exploded in front of cameras and reporters. In the early 1950s, his chief accomplishment was the Viking rocket, but it was even smaller than the Redstone, and he was never a serious contender to build a military super missile.

The Air Force had only one realistic choice, the man who had led their post-war program before it was cancelled: Karel Jan "Charlie" Bossart. Drawing on his experience in aeronautical engineering, he had continued to work on the problem of long-range rockets, even after the military had given up. Without his ideas, it is likely that America would have been years behind the Soviet union in deploying a working ICBM.

Charlie began from first principles, proposing a design that bore no resemblance to the missiles that von Braun had built. It would contain no internal structural support, no fuel tanks, just a thin stainless-steel hull filled with fuel and inflated by internal gas pressure. As the first Atlas was being readied at Cape Canaveral, some engineers feared its radical light-weight structure might disintegrate in flight.

But his design proved to be remarkably strong. Over two hundred of the ICBMs were deployed in the following years, and after it was retired from military duty, the rocket had a long history as a space vehicle for NASA. Charlie Bossart was briefly famous, hailed as the "Father of the Atlas" in the newspapers. He won numerous awards and was regarded as one of the finest technical men in the country. While he is still admired by experts, as one of the most innovative rocket designers in history, his name is no longer remembered by the general public.

1
Son of the Heather

What is a "rocket scientist?" The colloquialism has come to mean anyone of extraordinary genius, but it especially refers to outstanding pioneers of rocketry and space exploration. Technically speaking, most of those men were not professional scientists—Karel Bossart and the designer of the Soviet ICBM were both aeronautical engineers.

The more interesting question is what *makes* a rocket scientist? Of the thousands of men who worked on aircraft design, few left a well-established field to set out in an unexplored and uncertain direction. Few had the creativity and confidence to design machines of an entirely new kind, with no guidebook to follow. And even in the adolescent field of rocketry, the design of Karel's Atlas missile broke with convention and stirred controversy. But while there are many books about the rocket, relatively little has been written about the mastermind behind it. A naturalized citizen of the United States, his unusual upbringing began in Belgium.

The Bossart family had lived in Antwerp for several generations. A city with a long history, in medieval times, *Borgt aen 'twerp* ("fortress on the bank") was situated on a bend in the wide Scheldt River. It was an ideal inland port, 55 miles upstream from the North Sea. By the 16th century, Antwerp was the world's first global market and banking center.[1] Sugar from the West Indies, textiles from England, and traders from Portugal, Spain and Italy arrived at its docks.

---

[1] Robinson, Wilfrid, *Antwerp: An Historical Sketch*, Washbourne, London, 1904.; Cammaerts, Emile, *Belgium: From the Roman Invasion to the Present Day*, Fischer Unwin, London, 1921.

Antwerp's first golden age of prosperity was followed by two centuries of hardship and oppression. In the late 1500's, Belgium came under the rule of Spain, then the Austrian Empire. Its neighbor to the north was the hostile Dutch Republic, which blockaded the mouth of the Scheldt. But by the 19th century, Antwerp was once again a peaceful and wealthy trading center, the third busiest port in Europe (rivaled only by London and Liverpool).

Karel's grandfather worked as a storeman in the dock-side warehouses. Lodewijk Philip Bossart[2] lived just a few hundred feet from the river, above a café on a street called the Veemarkt. Today the Veemarkt is a park, but in Lodewijk's time the wide brick street was a busy cattle market, filled with the sounds and smells of animal herds, livestock auctions, and butchers plying their trade. At night, commerce of a less reputable variety took over the street, as the neighborhood became a busy red-light district for visiting sailors.[3]

In 1874, Lodewijk married Joanna Van Horenbeek,[4] the daughter of a tobacco merchant, and they started to raise a family. But after several years, he contracted a debilitating pulmonary disease. When Karel's father was born, Lodewijk was too ill to be present when the birth was recorded. He died at the age of 39, leaving behind a 22-year-old widow and three toddler sons.

In the overcrowded working-class neighborhood where the Bossarts lived, diseases like tuberculosis were all too common, and a diphtheria epidemic was sweeping Belgium at the time. Both diseases were especially deadly to young children and the elderly. A few months following Lodewijk's death, two of his sons also died. After that, his surviving son Louis[5] was raised by his mother as an only child. With help from aunts and uncles, his mother was able to support them as a shop keeper in Mechelen, a small city south of Antwerp. She was a strong-willed woman, though sometimes short-tempered.[6]

Having lived in such a rough neighborhood, Louis and his mother were eager to ascend to the middle-class and escape the life they had next to the docks. More than the making of money, Louis came to embrace education

---

[2] Ludovicus Philippus Bossart (1839-1878). In those days, Latin forms of names were used in very formal documents like birth or marriage certificates. A French form, Louis Philip, would be used for most official purposes, and he would be called Lodewijk by his Flemish friends and family. In French, the family name is pronounced bo-SART, which is how Karel's sister still pronounced it. In Flemish it is said like BOSS-art, which is how Karel and his American family say it.

[3] Hoste, Peter, *De Veemarkt*, Eindwerk stadsgids Antwerpen, 2003.

[4] Joanna Catharine Van Horenbeek (1856-1919).

[5] Ludovicus ("Louis") Carolus Joannes Bossart (1875-1950).

[6] Karel's sister remembered her years later, smashing dishes during an angry argument.

and intellectual society as a means to improve his life. After graduating from college in Lier in 1894, he began a career as a municipal school teacher His first job was assistant instructor at the Kasteel Street boy's school No. 23, which paid a modest salary of 1500 Belgian Francs.

In a few years, he met and fell in love with a like-minded school teacher, a graduate from the college at Bruges named Carolina Tyck.[7] Her father was a harbor worker who probably labored since childhood; official documents indicate he could not read or write. After a year-long engagement, the couple married in 1902, in a civil ceremony at Antwerp's town hall. Their first home was a small apartment above a shop on Isabella Street, where their son Karel Jan Bossart was born on the morning of February 9, 1904.

As soon as they had the means, they found nicer accommodations. One of Louis's friends owned a jewelry store on "The Meir," Antwerp's busy shopping thoroughfare. A few years after Karel's birth, the family moved to an apartment above the store, overlooking Otto Venius Street. Their new home was big enough for Louis's mother to move in with them, occupying one of the two bedrooms. This would be their home base in the city throughout Karel's youth and young adult years.

Karel's upbringing was profoundly affected by his parents' intellectual activism. They were involved in radical education reform, early nature conservation movements, and most of all in a movement to advance the culture of the Flemish language.

The Bossarts, like most residents of the northern half of Belgium, spoke the Flemish dialect of Dutch (i.e., the language of Flanders). In the south, the majority language was French. In the prosperous 16th century, Flemish had been the principal language. However, in the 19th century, it was French-speaking culture that dominated Belgium, and Flemish was viewed as an inferior language of rural peasants. Many middle-class Antwerp families were Flemish speaking, but they peppered their speech with French words to demonstrate sophistication. Nevertheless, a few intellectuals were intent on restoring Flemish to its former importance and cleansing it of French influences.

At the heart of the Flemish culture movement in Antwerp was Frans Franck, a wealthy designer, decorator and art merchant. Franck took the young Louis Bossart under his wing,[8] introducing him to artists and cultural elites, such as the famous illustrator James Ensor and Soviet film maker

---

[7] Carolina Tyck (1874-1952).
[8] Dora Bossart, video interviews.

Sergei Eisenstein. The painter Richard Baeseleer was a witness at Louis and Caroline's wedding, and their best friend was a furniture maker and cultural activist named Jef Van Overloop. In 1899, Franck and Van Overloop were among the founders of *De Kapel*,[9] a freewheeling argumentative society of revolutionaries, anarchists, Flamingants (Flemish nationalists) and occult mystics. The name referred to the disused chapel that Franck rented for their weekly meetings. *De Kapel* was succeeded by *Kunst van Heden* ("Art of Today"), a society for the appreciation of modern Flemish art and culture, more middle-class and less radical than its predecessor. Louis eventually became the society's secretary, and he wrote articles in the cultural magazine *Vlaanderen*,[10] sharing his thoughts about Flemish life and the future of education.

When the nation of Belgium was created in 1830, largely by French-speaking citizens, Catholicism had been a major reason that many Flemish speakers had agreed to break away from the Netherlands. But the rise of Flemish nationalism was concurrent with growing secularism and freedom to criticize the church. Taking a personal and professional interest in the well-being of children, Louis published a book accusing the Belgian Catholic Church of exploiting the labor of orphans.[11] He detailed a vast clandestine industry, producing everything from beer to women's wear. Children as young as nine were put to work, and paid only about one franc per day. Not only was this unregulated and untaxed business an abuse of children, it put downward pressure on the wages of adult workers, especially in the garment industry. At least two books were published, to refute his criticism.[12] The Dominican Father Rutten denounced Louis's book as, "a vulgar anti-clerical pamphlet." But the Belgian Liberal Party, which opposed the political power of the Catholic Church, endorsed his work and called for stronger child labor laws.[13]

Years later, in America, Karel would politely list his religion as Presbyterian, but like his father, he mistrusted organized religious establishments and "never darkened the door of a church."[14]

The northern suburb, Kalmthout,[15] was a popular semi-rural retreat for artists and the upper middle class of Antwerp, and in particular it was

---

[9] Resseler, Walter & Hugo, *Natuur- en Stedenschoon en de kunststromingen rond 1910*, www.kvns.be.

[10] *Vlaanderen : maandschrift voor de Vlaamsche letterkunde*, 1906(3, 4), 1907(5, 11).

[11] Bossart, Louis, *L'industrie et le commerce des congrégations en Belgique*, 1913.

[12] Rutten, Le Père, *Le Travail Dans Les Couvents. Réponse Au Livre De M. Bossart, 1914*.; Fr.-G. Franken, *Een brief over het werk van den heer Bossart*, 1914.

[13] *Het Volksbelang*, January 17, 1914.

[14] Myrle Ann and Newell Bossart, *personal communication*, 2014.

[15] Pronounced "CAL-em-tout" in the Antwerp dialect.

fashionable among Louis's intellectual cohorts. A few years after Karel's birth, Louis bought land from a farmer and had a one-story brick house built. Over the years, he added to the structure, eventually arriving at a somewhat eccentric three-story home, including a greenhouse in the back. Things were going well for Louis; his career was advancing, he was a land owner, and his status in the Flemish intellectual community was on the rise.

The countryside was a big change from the bustling center of the city. The Bossarts embraced the rural lifestyle, filling the large back yard with pathways, gardens and fruit trees, and even selling some of the produce to the locals. Their friends the Van Overloops purchased a home next door. Often sharing breakfast or dinner with the Bossarts, they were honorary "Uncle Jef" and "Aunt Vire."[16] Karel often had long talks with Jef, over games of chess, and their son Jan Van Overloop was his best friend.

In 1911, the Bossart family had a bad turn of fortune. Louis became ill with fever and a chronic cough, and the doctor confirmed what he must have feared: tuberculosis. Very likely, this was the disease that killed Louis's father. He may have caught it from a child at school, and it could have lain dormant for years. Almost forgotten today, then it was a plague on the rich and the poor. Robert Koch, the Nobel laureate and discoverer of the tubercle bacillus, wrote that it was a bigger killer than any of the most dreaded diseases such as bubonic plague and cholera. In the early 20th century, tuberculosis killed one in seven people living in Europe and the United States.[17]

For the poor and working class, tuberculosis was a death sentence, but even before antibiotics, there was a good cure rate for those who could afford proper care. Starting in October, Louis spent several months at one of the famous sanatoriums of Davos, Switzerland. In the high altitude valley, doctors believed the rarified alpine air and baths in the mountain water would stimulate circulation in the lungs. Patients were given nutritious food and plenty of rest outdoors in deck chairs piled with blankets.

Louis's illness was a crisis for the family. He was such a dominating force in Karel's life, it is hard to imagine how different his life would have been if his father had passed away when he was just a young boy. But fortunately, Louis recovered and was able to return to Antwerp. Because of the damage to his lungs, he was unable to resume the exertion of classroom speaking. He semi-retired, took a pension and did administrative work for the school system. His doctor advised him to spend more time in the clean

---

[16] Charlie mentions that they called her "Klein Tante Vire" in a letter to their son Jan.
[17] *Questions and Answers about Tuberculosis*, CDC, 2014.

air of their country home, and the Bossarts tried living in Kalmthout year round. But they soon discovered it was much more convenient and comfortable to winter at their Antwerp apartment.

In the summer of 1913, the Bossarts had their second child, a daughter named Dora. Born in Kalmthout, she was a welcomed addition to the family, even though Karel sometimes had to skip playing with his friends to babysit his new sister.

About this time, Louis began teaching at an alternative school run by the Diesterweg Society in Kalmthout. The Bossarts were founding members of the society, which advocated open-air lectures, immersing children in nature, physical exercise, and co-educational classrooms of boys and girls.[18] His wife also taught there for a few years, and then returned to the Antwerp school system as head mistress of the Girl's School No. 13, on Van Aerdt Street. Carolina worked there until her retirement in 1930.[19]

Not surprisingly, Louis applied his ideas about education and language to Karel. He believed that Flemish children should be educated in their native tongue, but not Flemish as it was then spoken by people in Antwerp, which thought had become bastardized with French words and expressions. He wanted his son to grow up speaking the pure language.

Karel had started out in the municipal school system, attending 1st grade at Boy's School No. 14 on Albert Street, and in 2nd grade his father was his teacher there.[20] But after that, Louis and Carolina decided to undertake home schooling of their son. Before his parents left in the morning, they would leave a daily study assignment. As Karel later told the story, he would fool around all day, and then quickly do his lessons about an hour before his parents returned home.[21]

Karel demonstrated an aptitude for science and math, subjects that Louis specialized in teaching. The boy started a science club with his friends, and they spent much of their allowances on purchasing chemicals. He and Jan Van Overloop built and fired small rockets from his back yard, and more than a few experiments ended in explosions.[22] Botany was Louis's favorite topic, and the garden and the wild surrounding landscape was an ideal open-air classroom. He took Karel and his Diesterweg classes on tours

---

[18] *Diesterweg's Hulpkas voor Behoeftige Schoolkinderen,* Liberaal Archief, Ghent.

[19] Antwerp school records, curtesy of Saskia De Schepper.

[20] Letter from a teacher and friend of his mother, Jan Verbeeck, to Karel Bossart, October 21, 1963.

[21] "The Atlas Story," *The San Diego Union,* Special Reprint, Feb, 1958.; Verbeeck, Jan, Letter to Karel J. Bossart, Oct 21, 1963 (one of his teachers at Albert Street).

[22] De Bruyn, Frans, *De Klap Op De Vuurpijl,* Antwerp, 1964.

to teach them about the local flora, and his lectures inspired a life-long respect for nature in many of his students.[23]

The shady tree-lined road that ran past the Bossart house was aptly named *Duinzichtlei* ("Dune-View Lane"). Only a hundred yards away was the Kalmthout Heath, a vast wilderness of heather fields, peat bogs, sand dunes, and patches of gnarled scots pines, oaks and silver birch. This was where Karel and his friends spent so much of their youth, playing and taking long bicycle and walking excursions. He loved this landscape so much, decades later he told a reporter, "I am a son of the heather!"[24]

In Roman times the heath had been a dense primeval forest of oak and birch. It was the northern tip of the vast *Silva Carbonaria* that originally defined the eastern boundary of Belgium. As the name (the charcoal forest) implied, it was exploited as a source of fuel, and consequently almost none of it exists today. In Kalmthout, centuries of harvesting wood and digging peat had catastrophically transformed the landscape into its present form, too wet and infertile for building or farming. The Bossarts were actively involved in the politics and ecology of the heath, and along with many of their neighbors, they joined the Society for the Preservation of Nature and Clean Cities.[25] The society made the heath one of its priorities, and it stopped further destruction of the landscape, such as industrial mining of sand.

Organized sports were not a common form of play for children in those days, and Karel had little interest in them, but he was an avid outdoorsman and physically fit. During a game of hide and seek, he eluded his friends by chimneying to the ceiling of a hallway, pressing his hands and feet against the opposite walls. He was able to walk on his hands up and down the stairs of their Kalmthout home, and as a middle-aged man, he delighted in demonstrating this ability. Coins rained from his pockets, while nieces and nephews looked on in astonishment.[26]

Sailing was a life-long love of Karel's. One of his teenage playmates was Hugo Van Kuyck, the son of a wealthy French-speaking family who owned a summer mansion in Kalmthout. Hugo built a kayak with his friends and sailed on the Scheldt with his family's yacht.[27] Although Karel remembered him as something of a bully,[28] it was Hugo who introduced him to sailing.

---

[23] Florquin, Joos, *Ten Huize Van... VI*, 1970. (The producer of a famous TV show in Belgium)

[24] "Ik ben een zoon van de heide. Op de maan zal men nooit iets vinden, dat met de heide te vergelijken is." (unidentified Antwerp newspaper, 1963).

[25] *Vereeniging tot Behoud van Natuur- en Stedenschoon.* The society has been active since 1910 in environmental preservation in Belgium.

[26] Katherine Baum Wolpe, *personal communications*, 2013.

[27] Schelfhout, Charles Emmanuel, *Hugo van Kuyck: Le Belge qui conquit les plages normandes avant les armées allies*, 2004.

Decades later, Kuyck's knowledge of the northern coast of Belgium and France made him an important consultant for the allied invasion of Normandy.

Louis permitted and encouraged wholesome exploration, but at the end of the day, Karel was expected to report about where he had gone and what he had done. Although an intellectual free thinker, Louis was strict in the old-fashioned tradition of child rearing. Karel later described his father's attitude as "children spoke only when spoken to." He was also not a fan of contemporary popular culture. His daughter Dora recalled that he dismissed things such as jazz music and comic books with the Belgian phrase, *flauwe kul* (fiddlesticks!).[29] He did not permit his children to participate in holidays and popular celebrations that were related to causes he did not approve of, and he was very selective about whom they could befriend. Mostly, Karel and Dora played with the children of Louis's friends. While Kalmthout was a hang-out for intellectuals and the upper class, its native population were simple folk, and Louis believed his children would pick up bad attitudes and superstitions from them. Sensitive about his proletariat background, he forbade Dora from taking up knitting, looking down on such labor as beneath their social status (but later in life, it became an avid hobby of hers).

As both the parent and teacher, Louis had an overwhelming influence on his son, and he established many of the boy's interests and values. Karel embraced his father's curiosity and rational free thinking. But he rejected his parental authoritarianism and class snobbery, which were contradictions with his progressive philosophy.

Karel was only ten years old when Belgium's comfortable prosperity was shattered by the First World War. In the summer of 1914, the Bossart family was vacationing with some of their neighbors in the North Sea resort town of Ostend, 60 miles west of Antwerp. They rented an apartment half a block from the broad white beaches. One-year-old Dora first began walking on her own while they were there, and Karel spent the days swimming in the sea.

In June, the assassination of Archduke Ferdinand, the heir to the Austrian throne, by Serbian nationalists had initiated a chain of increasingly dire events: Austria threatened Serbia, Russia supported their fellow Slavs in Serbia, Germany allied with Austria and Russia allied with France. Belgium was neutral, but Germany declared war against Belgium, on August 4,

---

[28] Letter from Karel to Dora, April 20, 1969.
[29] Dora Scott and her sons, *personal communication,* December, 2012.

because they refused passage of the German army across to France. Consequently, Britain declared war on Germany to honor their defense treaty with Belgium. As allies and colonies joined in, the war spread around the globe.

Karel's parents tried to keep concerns about war from alarming the children. A week after the invasion of Belgium began, Louis wrote to his mother who was staying in their Antwerp apartment, advising her to stock up on provisions for the winter and to pick the fruit and rhubarb in the garden at Kalmthout, before it could be looted. If they were unable to get home, he told her to get help from the Van Overloops.

At the time of Louis's letter, the fortress of Liege had come under attack. Putting up unexpected military resistance, the Belgians foiled Germany's plan for a quick invasion of France. Louis considered taking his family across the English Channel on the Ostend-to-Dover ferry, but the boat was commandeered by the Belgian government. As long as fighting remained farther south, Ostend was relatively safe,[30] but the Germans soon turned their attention to Antwerp.

At that time, Antwerp was the most heavily fortified city in the world. Realizing that its army could never stand up against France or Germany, Belgium had developed the strategic plan to concentrate its defenses in one city, so in an emergency it could withdraw the army and government into an impregnable "National Redoubt."

In the 1860s, a high rampart had been built around Antwerp, with gun emplacements every kilometer. Beyond the wall, a moat around the city could be flooded by opening locks on the Scheldt. A few miles from the rampart, a ring of 9 large fortresses was built. However, not long after they were completed, it became clear that these forts were too close to the city, given the rapidly increasing range of artillery. In 1906 construction began on an outer ring of 22 heavy concrete forts. With walls 12 feet thick, topped with steel cupolas housing canons, the forts were engineered to resist the most powerful artillery known at the time: the French 10-inch caliber mortar.[31] These fortifications were considered a wonder of the modern world in 1914.

However, the first German attack on the city bypassed its formidable ground defenses. On August 25, Antwerp became the first city in the world to be bombed by aircraft. At 1 am, cruising at 2000 feet, a German Zeppelin probed the streets and buildings with a search light. It was the Kaiser's new airship, Z-9. Over 500 feet long, it consisted of an

---

[30] Letters from Louis Bossart to his mother, August 12 1914 and September 4.
[31] Rolf, Rudi and Peter Saal, *Fortress Europe*, Airlife Publishing, 1988.

aerodynamic aluminum framework covered with canvas. Inside were 18 gas cells holding 800,000 cubic feet of hydrogen. Lift was generated by two tons of hydrogen, which displaced 30 tons of air. The Zeppelin was self-propelled by three 200-horsepower engines and capable of a top speed of 50 miles per hour. Although it could carry only one ton of bombs, that was significantly more than a contemporary single-man fighter plane.

Dropping 6 and 8-inch artillery shells, Z-9 hit the St. Elisabeth military hospital. Another strike killed a family in their home. Six foot craters were left in streets, and one of the bombs destroyed an apartment building only a hundred yards from King Albert's Antwerp residence. Frustrated soldiers fired pistols into the air, to no avail. Z-9 was a particular menace to Belgian and British positions over the next weeks.[32] After the first attack, the city initiated night-time blackouts to make it more difficult for airships to locate their targets.

On September 2, a second Zeppelin attacked: this time, the repurposed passenger liner "Sachsen." Flying from a base in Cologne, it waited outside Antwerp, hovering at an altitude of 5500 feet, until the moon set. A little before 4 am, it dropped seven bombs on the city, its primary target being the central railway terminus.[33] The "Sachsen" was commanded by Ernst Lehmann, who survived many reconnaissance and bombing missions in the war. Ironically, he died in 1937 as a passenger on the Hindenburg.

Aerial warfare had been predicted by the French science fiction author Jules Verne and the English author H.G. Wells.[34] Only a few years after the first flight by the Wright brothers, the importance of aircraft was obvious to military leaders in Europe. The German imperial flying corps was created in 1910, as was the French *Armée de l'Air*. The British army and navy formed small flying forces in 1912.

During the war, 88 military Zeppelins were commissioned for the army and navy, but this fleet consumed valuable war-time resources. The hydrogen gas cells were made from paper-thin cow gut, a material needed in such large quantities that Germany had to outlaw the making of sausage casings. The strategic value of the slow, flammable Zeppelins was questionable, especially after the British began equipping their fighter planes with incendiary bullets.

As scientifically fascinating as the Zeppelins were, a more decisive weapons technology in World War I was artillery. To the surprise of

[32] Grahame-White, Claude and Harry Harper, "Zeppelin Airships: Their Record in the War," *The Fortnightly Review*, September 1915.; Various articles in *The New York Times*, 1914.
[33] Lehmann, Captain Ernst A. and Howard Mingos, *The Zeppelins*, Sears, 1927.
[34] Verne, Jules, *Robur le Conquérant*, Hetzel, Paris, 1886; Wells, Herbert George, *The War in the Air*, Bell & Sons, London, 1908.

military experts, the famous fortifications of Belgium could not withstand a new generation of guns developed by Krupp, Germany's armament corporation. Early in the invasion, they attacked Fort Loncin, and a shell broke through its cement ceiling and detonated the ammunition magazine. The entire garrison was instantly entombed. After the war, no attempt was made to dig up the ruins, and the site was declared a national cemetery.

Especially important was the new 16-inch-caliber howitzer, called "Big Bertha" (*Dicke Bertha* in German). It was originally developed as a naval gun, but then adapted to use as field artillery, mounted on a mobile platform. Sounding like an express train, the incoming shells carried a ton of high explosive, and the bombardment methodically pulverized the Belgian defenses. Ceaseless concussions against the concrete roofs stunned and confused soldiers inside, driving some of them to nervous breakdowns.

One of the gun's developers, Captain Karl Becker, described its terrible effect against Antwerp's outer fortress of Wavre St. Catherine:

> *Now it was time to direct the telescope upon the air just above the target; with a little practice the shell could be picked up in the air and the impact itself observed. On this day, I saw my eleventh shot strike fair upon the top of the cupola, where the enemy's guns were actively firing. There was a quick flash, which we had learned at Kummersdorf to recognize as the impact of steel upon steel. Then an appreciable pause, during which the cupola seemed uninjured; then a great explosion. After a few minutes the smoke began to clear, and in place of the cupola we saw a black hole, from which dense smoke was still pouring. Half the cupola stood upright, 50 metres away; the other half had fallen to the ground. The shell, fitted with a delayed action fuse, had exploded inside.*[35]

Captain Becker had a doctorate in engineering and was one of Germany's leading experts in ballistics. While his work on artillery had an obvious effect on the Bossart family during World War I, his subsequent work would have an even bigger influence on Karel's future career: after the war, it would be Becker who conceived of and led the army rocket program that created the V-2 missile.

The Bossarts were still in Ostend during the aerial attacks on Antwerp, but Louis decided it was best for the family to return home while it was still possible. He was not sure if it would be safer to stay in their apartment or

---

[35] Becker, Captain Karl, "The 42-cm Mortar: Fact and Fancy," *The Field Artillery Journal*, May-June, 1922.

move out to the country home. If necessary, they could cross the heath to neutral Netherlands, whose border was less than two miles from their house.[36] The Bossart country home was north of the city, and luckily for them, the German offensive came from the south.

On September 29, 1914, the siege of Antwerp began. As it proceeded, the outer fortresses in the south were reduced to rubble, one by one. Bridges over the Nete River were strategically blown up by the retreating Belgian army, but on October 5 the Germans were able to cross the river and begin to attack the inner ring of fortresses.[37] Soon, they were close enough to begin shelling Antwerp itself, just before midnight on October 7. Eventually 200 siege guns were brought in, including Big Berthas. Against unreinforced civilian structures, the large projectiles could level entire buildings with a single strike.[38] To make matters worse, the city waterworks were blown up, making it difficult to fight numerous fires started by the barrage.

Karel never forgot the sight of Antwerp burning. When the shelling began, Louis loaded a cart with supplies, and the Bossarts began moving out to their country house. Along the way, they reached a vantage point to view the bombardment. Burning oil tanks on the river bank illuminated the sky. Shells flew near the 400-foot tower of Our Lady Cathedral, but luckily, the most distinctive feature of the city skyline was never hit. Zeppelins hovered above the city, dropping bombs and directing artillery strikes by radio. The 10-year-old boy was more fascinated than afraid of what he saw. It must have appeared like a scene out of science fiction.

In the midst of the bombardment, two British Sopwith biplanes took off from Antwerp's airport. Their destination was the Zeppelin hangar in Düsseldorf. Each was carrying two 20-pound Hale bombs, tossed from the cockpit by the pilot. The sensitive hair trigger was armed by rotation of a propeller as it fell through the air. After a couple unsuccessful passes, one of the bombs found its target. Once ignited, the hydrogen fireball rose 500 feet and burned so quickly that the hangar itself was almost undamaged. But all that remained of the hated Z-9 airship was a tangle of aluminum trusswork.[39]

After thirty hours of shelling, the mayor surrendered the city on the morning of October 9. The German general was disappointed to find that

---

[36] Letter from Louis Bossart to his mother, September 4, 1914.
[37] Commandant De Gerlache de Gommery, "The Capture of Antwerp," *Source Records of the Great War*, 1923.
[38] Powell, E. Alexander, "The Taking of Antwerp," *Scribner's Magazine*, January 1915.
[39] "British Airship Raid Destroys A Zeppelin," *The New York Times*, October 10, 1914.

the Belgian government and most of the army had escaped across the Scheldt on a pontoon bridge, which they torpedoed behind them.

The Bossart family remained in their Kalmthout home, sometimes crossing the heath to buy butter and supplies in The Netherlands. After the spring of 1915, those trips were made impossible by a 2000-volt electric fence along the Belgian/Netherlands border. Locals called it *Dodendraad*— the wire of death. An estimated 850 people were killed by the fence during the war, either electrocuted or shot by the guards who patrolled its length.

Although damaged by the siege, Antwerp was spared the total devastation of the war's frontline. But all of Belgium was threatened by the danger of famine. That disaster was averted by the Committee for Relief in Belgium (CRB), founded by the wealthy American engineer Herbert Hoover. He pressured the British and German governments into allowing food ships through the allied naval blockade. Over the next four years, the CRB brought 5 million tons of food into the war-ravaged country, prompting one British official to describe Hoover's organization as a "benevolent pirate fleet." This would not be the last time that Hoover touched the life of Karel Bossart.

For the Bossarts, the German occupation was a hardship, but life went on. Louis's beloved Flemish cultural movement was tested, when Germany tried to exploit the divide between French-speaking and Flemish-speaking Belgians. The Germans promoted the idea that the Flemish people were their racial cousins, and a few of the more radical Flamingants embraced that idea and collaborated with the enemy. But overwhelmingly, Belgians united in the face of Germany's numerous atrocities.

The occupation of Antwerp lasted the entire war, until the signing of the armistice on November 11, 1918. After years of stalemated trench warfare, Germany was exhausted, dealing with increasing dissent and war-weariness at home, and facing vast numbers of new troops entering the war from America. Afterward, Europe was left dramatically changed: the monarchies of Germany, Austria, Turkey and Russia all perished. The Bolshevik Revolution in Russia drove a wave of talented people out of that country, to settle in Europe and America (including many aeronautical engineers).

What Karel witnessed during the siege of Antwerp left a lasting impression. He had seen the military power of aircraft first hand.[40] After the war, like many boys, he was fascinated by aviation exhibitions and the stories of dare-devil pilots and aerial dog fights.

---

[40] "The Atlas Story," *The San Diego Union*, Special Reprint, Feb, 1958.

One thing that had continued without interruption during the war was Karel's home schooling. In September of 1919, Karel rode the train to Brussels to take the entrance exam of the Free University (*Université Libre de Bruxelles* or ULB). He was only 15, but his parents had accelerated his education aggressively, and they believed he was ready for college. Unfortunately, he failed the French-language section of the exam, and courses at the university were taught only in the official national language. Ghent University taught in Flemish, but despite his Flemish nationalism, Louis insisted that ULB was the best, and so that was where Karel must go. His son likely had no say in the matter.

Karel's pure-Flemish education had left him less familiar with French than most educated Belgians; he had not begun learning it until he was 14. After he failed the entrance exam, Louis decided that his son needed total immersion in the language, so he sent him to live in Paris for six months. Karel stayed with an elderly woman in Bourg-la-Reine, a friend of the Bossart family who did not speak a word of Flemish. While there, Karel attended the Lycée Lakanal, a prestigious high school for gifted students. It shared many features of the Diesterweg school, such as outdoor classes, exposure to nature and physical fitness as well as first-class training in science. Karel also took the time to make sight-seeing trips in France, and he sent his sister letters filled with humorous drawings depicting his life in Paris. He had not been entirely happy with his father's plan, but when he took the ULB exam the next year, he passed and was admitted.

The summer before he started college, Karel made his first trip to North America; in this case to Canada. It was made possible by someone who had a great influence on his life, his mother's youngest sister Vire. Only 13 years older than Karel, Vire was more of a big sister to the boy than an aunt.[41] As a young woman, Vire wanted to see the world, and so she got a job as a waitress on the Red Star and Canadian Pacific steamship lines. That was where she met her fiancé, an English steward named Russell Dent. During Karel's summer holiday break, she got her nephew a job on one of her voyages.[42] Many years later, Vire's daughter wrote, "Since that time, there must have been a kind of conspiracy between those two," describing how Aunt Vire had encouraged Karel's adventurous nature, "She showed him the way to the U.S.A."

Of course, the sea voyage would not have happened without his father's approval. Louis was a strict parent, but he did not stifle his son's

---

[41] Elvire Maria Tyck (1891-1966). Note that his mother's youngest sister and their neighbor Mrs. Van Overloop were both called "Aunt Vire." Vire and Russell were married that fall, 1920.

[42] Dent, Daisy, Letter to Newell Bossart, October 20, 1975.; Bastiaensen, Jean, "Kalmthout en de vader van de Atlasraket," *Calmpthoutania*, No. 1, 2000.

personal development. Like sending his son to school in Paris, the job on an ocean liner must have struck Louis as educational and character-building. Furthermore, it was socially acceptable work. Louis knew the owners of the steamship line, who were wealthy patrons of *Kunst van Heden*.

In early June of 1920, the SS Grampian set out down the Scheldt, with a thousand passengers and a new 16-year-old bellboy. Before departure, Karel would have helped load provisions on the ship, and once they were underway, he was expected to look sharp, wait on passengers and help the stewards with a variety of service and clean-up jobs. The cruise began down the Scheldt and into the English Channel for a stop at Southampton, and then out into the rough waters of the North Atlantic. Even in the summer, the trip was not without some hazard; the Grampian had collided with a small iceberg the year before.

The crossing of the Atlantic was without incident, but Karel almost failed to survive his stay in Canada. The ship steamed up the St. Lawrence River, docking at Quebec City on June 19. A few days later, it moored at the massive concrete Victoria Pier, in Montreal. The pier's famous war-memorial clock tower was under construction that summer. While staying there, Karel went swimming in the river and was caught in its strong currents. Luckily, his companions rescued him before he was swept away and possibly drowned.

Karel was just 16 when he started college in Brussels. His father had already decided that his son would major in mining or civil engineering, because a degree in those fields would guarantee a job in the Belgian civil service. Belgium was not resource-rich, but in those days it was actively mining coal and zinc. The curriculum was broad, including some basic science: chemistry, geology, mineralogy, prospecting, assaying. The engineering problems of mining were taught, including tunneling, blasting, structural supports, ventilation, and pumping.

While attending the school, Karel lived with Mrs. Van Overloop's sister and her husband, and he often took the train home for the weekends. His sister idolized him and looked forward to seeing him. Unlike Karel, she was attending public school, and it was a special treat if he could walk her to class on Saturday mornings (in Antwerp, children attended school six days a week).

Karel graduated in 1925 with a degree in mining engineering[43] and membership in the school's association of engineers.[44] However, in his last year at the university, having completed the requirements for the

[43] I.C.M – Ingénieur Civil des Mines
[44] A.I.Br. – Association des Ingénieurs sortis de l'Université Libre de Bruxelles

engineering degree, Karel elected to take an optional course in aeronautics, and that changed his life.

The course was taught by Belgian aviation pioneer, Emile Allard. Allard had started work in the steel industry, but his fascination with airplanes led him to resign in 1909, when he moved to France to get a pilot license and study the principles of airplane design. With his background in metallurgy, he was especially interested in alternatives to wooden aircraft construction. Working with a Belgian airplane company, he built one of the world's first all-metal monoplanes. In addition to his duties as professor, Allard established and headed the Institute for Aerodynamic Research at Sint-Genesius-Rode, near Brussels.

Allard's *cours d'aeronautique* revitalized Karel's boyhood interest in aviation. Just as Allard had done, Karel decided to change his career direction. In his first major rebellion against his father, he decided to pursue aircraft design instead of becoming a mining engineer.

After taking the class in aeronautics, Karel thought of an interesting way to use the knowledge. He loved sailing, and he wondered if a boat could be optimally designed by applying aircraft-engineering theory. It was the first demonstration of his remarkable style of technical thinking: taking a familiar problem and starting from scratch, ignoring the traditional solutions to see if something new could outperform conventional designs.

He posed the problem in a simple abstract way, imagining two fluids moving at different speeds, such as water with air blowing over its surface. He defined the boat as two airfoils (lift-generating wing shapes), one moving through the water and the other moving through the air (in other words, the keel and the sail). It was a novel idea to use an airfoil for the sail, a shape that had been optimized for lifting power by sophisticated mathematical analysis. It was more efficient than simply using a sail to catch the wind. The idea has been proved sound by modern high-performance sailing ships, such as the AC72 boats used in the America's Cup Race.

Karel derived a formula for the optimum size of the sail, and found it would have to be 800 times the area of the keel. That was problematic. Such a large sail would be tipped over by wind force, and its weight would sink the boat. To solve that problem, he separated the keel and sail into two parts: a flying airfoil connected by a cable to a remote-controlled keel floating in the water. The tethered sail would stay aloft like a kite. In August, 1925, he applied for a patent, which was granted a month later.[45]

---

[45] Bossart, C. *Appareil de locomotion utilisant l'énergie potentielle existant entre deux fluides en mouvement relatif l'un par rapport à l'autre* (Apparatus of locomotion using the potential energy existing between two fluids

Although he never built his decoupled sailboat, the idea of the kite ship has been realized in modern times, as an efficient way to augment cargo ships with wind power.[46]

An opportunity soon arose for further study in aeronautical engineering. After the war, Herbert Hoover's Committee for the Relief of Belgium liquidated its assets and used the cash, $9 million,[47] to repair war-damaged Belgian universities and establish a student exchange program. Encouraged by his professors, Karel applied for and received one of 26 CRB Graduate Fellowships awarded that year. He signed up to study at the Massachusetts Institute of Technology and was also granted a second year of financial aid so he could complete a master's degree. The scholarship program paid full tuition, first-class travel, and a stipend of $1000.

In addition to humanitarian goals, Hoover hoped his exchange program would promote the American philosophy of democracy and free enterprise. In that regard, Karel would be one of his success stories.

Some of his schoolmates thought he was crazy to go to America to study aviation. "Paris is the place for the airplane," a friend told him.[48] Although the first working airplane was invented by the Wright Brothers, aerial warfare during World War I accelerated the evolution of aircraft, and European manufacturers such as Fokker, Sopwith and Nieuport became the technology leaders. In the first year of the war, 1400 airplanes were built in France, 1000 in Germany, 800 in Russia and 400 in Britain. But only 23 were built in the United States.[49]

Nevertheless, Karel decided to attend school in America, since nobody was offering him a scholarship to Paris. However, one problem still remained: Karel had studied English a little, but he did not know the language well. The summer before leaving Antwerp, he enrolled in a six-week crash course at the Berlitz language center. Knowing Flemish and French, he found that English was not too difficult, and after the course, he continued practicing until he arrived in the United States.

Contrary to his friends' misgivings about American aeronautics, the Massachusetts Institute of Technology built an important program of education and research in the subject of airplanes and airships. In 1896, seven years before the flight of the Wright brothers, MIT built the first

---

in relative motion with respect to each other). Brevet No. 328,225, September 15, 1925.

[46] *Proceedings of the International Symposium on Windship Technology*, Southampton, UK, 1985.

[47] Comparable to $150 million today.

[48] Interview of Mr. K.J. Bossart by John L. Sloop, April 27, 1974.

[49] Arrighi, Robert, *Revolutionary Atmosphere*, NASA, 2010.

wind tunnel in the country. A simple device, powered by the building's ventilation system, it was used to follow up on the aerodynamics experiments of Samuel Langley. The first flying machines were lighter-than-air vehicles, rigid and non-rigid airships (i.e., Zeppelins and blimps). MIT's department of Naval Architecture and Marine Engineering considered airships to be within its purview and was the first to give aircraft serious attention.

In 1913, the department started an official graduate program in aeronautical engineering. Since there were few academic experts in the new field of aircraft design, they hired one of their own recent master of engineering graduates. Jerome Hunsaker began his new job by spending the summer and fall in Europe, where he met with experts in the theory and practice of flight. He spoke with Anthony Fokker, the renowned Dutch aircraft designer who would design fighter planes for Germany when war began the next year. Hunsaker tried to learn as much as possible about Zeppelins, but the Germans were secretive. He had to settle for making his professional observations of the airship surreptitiously, as a paying passenger. When he returned to America, he brought with him plans for a new wind tunnel, generously provided by the British National Physical Laboratory. One of his first students was Donald Douglas, who helped build the tunnel and went on to found Douglas Aircraft Company (later McDonnell Douglas).

By the time Karel arrived, in 1925, the institute had a solid aeronautics faculty. Hunsaker had left to design airships for the Navy. The new head of the program was Prof. Edward Pearson Warner, who had just become the chief scientist at the National Advisory Committee for Aeronautics (NACA).[50] Warner had built several new wind tunnels at MIT, the latest being a 7.5-foot diameter circular tunnel capable of testing models at 80 mph. In practice, the machine produced so much noise and vibration that it was rarely operated at full speed.

As a professor, Warner was rigorous, demanding and somewhat aloof. His skills in algebra and differential equations were intimidating, and students would spend an evening trying to understand a solution to a problem that Warner was able to write on the blackboard in minutes. He wore custom-made suits that had extra pockets, which were usually filled with multi-colored pens, notebooks and a slide rule.[51]

---

[50] Bilstein, Roger E., "Edward Pearson Warner and the New Air Age," *Aviation's Golden Age*, University of Iowa Press, 1989. NACA, founded in 1915 and became NASA in 1958.

[51] Wright, T.P., "Edward Pearson Warner, 1894-1958: An Appreciation", *Journal of the Royal Aeronautical Society*, October, 1958.

Helping Warner was Prof. Charles Burgess, one of America's foremost experts on Zeppelins and the son of a famous racing yacht designer. He had been a ship designer and then an airship designer for the Navy, and just prior to joining the institute, he had worked with Hunsaker on the ZR-1 *Shenandoah*, the first airship in the world to be inflated with helium. Airships were considered viable aircraft for passengers, military observation and even arctic research. That interest ended abruptly in 1937, after the Hindenburg Disaster.

Karel was enrolled in a two-year program for a Master of Science in Aeronautical Engineering (M.Sc.Ae). It included classes in theoretical and applied aerodynamics, lab time with the wind tunnel, airship theory, airplane engines, propeller theory, aircraft design, and the history of aeronautics.[52] While he was at MIT, the aeronautics program expanded sufficiently to offer an undergraduate major, titled Course XVI (i.e., a course of study comprised of multiple classes). MIT's modern-day astronautics program still bears that name. Warner left in 1926, and Charles Taylor was hired to head the department. Taylor was the former lead engine designer at Wright Aeronautical Corporation and one of the creators of the "Whirlwind" engine, which powered important aircraft such as the Fokker trimotor and Ford trimotor airliners. Fokker himself (who moved to America in 1922) gave a guest lecture during Karel's second term.

Classes in 1925 began at the end of September, and Karel arrived in New York City a week early, on the Red Star liner SS Zeeland. He chose a ship that carried economy-class passengers, because Hoover permitted his exchange students to travel more cheaply and get the difference in first-class ticket price added to their stipend. In Cambridge, he rented a room in a Victorian-style boarding house on Dana Street, about a mile from campus.

Karel was particularly interested in structural analysis and the properties of materials. Both Emile Allard and Prof. Warner worked in those areas, and they were involved in the challenge of constructing aircraft with metal instead of wood. Planes had to be as light as possible, and the first ones were built with spruce frameworks covered by canvas. But these materials had serious drawbacks. Wood could rot, it was flexible, and it could split along its grain if stressed in the wrong direction.

Metals were stronger and more rigid than wood, but heavier, so the style of wooden construction did not carry over to metal. Rather than thick beams, metal had to be fabricated into hollow tubes, trusses or corrugated sheets. As aircraft became larger, metal design became more and more

---

[52] *Catalogue For 1925-1926*, Massachusetts Institute of Technology, Vol. 60, 1925.

advantageous.[53] In Britain, aircraft engineers had experimented with steel, which was familiar and easy to work with. It was heavy but very strong. To achieve the same weight and strength as wooden structures, it had to be rolled very thin, and buckling was a danger.

In Germany, metallurgists had developed duralumin, an alloy of aluminum and copper that was ten times stronger than pure aluminum. It was much lighter than steel, but not as strong. The first major application of the new alloy was the framework of Zeppelins. It soon became one of the most popular materials for aircraft design, produced in sheets called "alclad," because they were bonded with a thin coating of pure aluminum for corrosion resistance.

While Karel was at MIT, Professor Warner was consulting for the U.S. Air Mail Service. During an inspection of the operations, Warner survived the crash of a Ford Stout 2-AT air transport plane. It was an early all-metal aircraft, built from duralumin with corrugated skin. The accident reinforced his belief that metal was the future of airplane materials. In his report, he told the Postmaster General that a conventional wooden structure would have caused fatal injuries in a similar crash.[54]

Outside of coursework, Karel was eager to explore the United States and learn about its people and culture. It was the "Roaring Twenties." The economy was booming, and in spite of the prohibition of alcohol, American society was going through a time of experimentation and permissiveness. It presented the young man with a level of freedom he had never experienced; not just freedom from the control of his father, but freedom from the conformity and formality of European society. Karel was a gregarious and confident individual who made friends fast and knew how to enjoy what America had to offer. He joined the Aeronautical Engineering Society, and he later remarked that these social connections helped his career throughout his life. On formal documents in the U.S.A., he used the French form of his name, "Charles," and he began to insist that people call him "Charlie."

During the summer break in 1926, Charlie decided to exercise his new-found liberty by exploring the country and making a pilgrimage to some of the centers of aircraft design and manufacture.[55] He bought a used Harley

[53] Warner, Edward, "Metal Construction of Aircraft," *Christian Science Monitor*, 1922.
[54] Bilstein, Roger E., "Edward Pearson Warner and the New Air Age", *Aviation's Golden Age*, University of Iowa Press, 1989.; Wright, T.P., "Edward Pearson Warner, 1894-1958: An Appreciation", *Journal of the Royal Aeronautical Society*, October, 1958.
[55] Shearer, Lloyd, "Charlie Bossart, Father of the Atlas," *Parade*, March 1, 1959.; Newell Bossart, *personal communication*, 2012.; Josseaud, Fernand, "Le vrai pere de la fuse Atlas!," *Panorama Hebdomadaire*

Davidson, an army-green motorcycle in doubtful condition, which he fixed up as best he could.

His first road trip was to Long Island and the new aircraft plant of Igor Sikorsky, a man who would play an important role later in Charlie's life. Famous today as an inventor of helicopters, in the 1920s and 1930s Sikorsky was a pioneer of large multi-engine passenger planes and seaplanes. In Russia, Sikorsky built the world's first four-engine aircraft, the S-21, which was capable of carrying half a dozen people. That was in 1913, when most airplanes were small single-man vehicles and some academics even believed that it was impossible to build an airplane heavier than one ton.[56] The next year, Sikorsky built the S-22, able to carry a dozen people. Its interior had wicker furniture and an onboard bathroom, almost unimaginable for an airplane of that time. In the West, some experts did not believe the reports of these gigantic aircraft. Designed as a passenger plane, it proved more useful as the world's first heavy bomber, and the Tsar's government built 75 of them during the war.

After the communist revolution, Sikorsky was warned by friends that he was on a list of political enemies, and he had to flee for his life. He arrived in New York City in 1919, with $600 in his pocket. The Russian composer and pianist Sergei Rachmaninoff lent him money to start over and establish a new business in America, building and selling large aircraft. With the help of escaped engineers, pilots and even a Russian prince, he built the prototype airplane S-29A in 1923. Some of the parts were scrounged from a local junkyard, but the two-engine plane flew and could carry 14 passengers. Their base of operation was supplied by a refugee from the revolution, a former flying ace in the Russian navy who owned a chicken farm in Hempstead. The birds were constantly underfoot around the work, and chicken was frequently prepared for dinner. It was not unusual to find rivets in the gizzards.

When Charlie visited the Sikorsky Manufacturing Company in 1926, they had moved from the chicken farm to a wooden hangar on Roosevelt Field, near Mineola, Long Island. They were busy working on the S-35, a large biplane with two engines and a 101-foot wingspan. It was an all-metal plane, made from duralumin and steel.

Sikorsky was preparing the S-35 to take on a famous challenge of the day: the Orteig Prize. In 1919, the wealthy New York businessman Raymond Orteig had offered a $25,000 reward for the first non-stop airplane flight between New York and Paris (in either direction).[57] Sikorsky

---

pour la famille No. 22., May 30, 1959.
[56] Sikorsky, Igor, *The Story of the Winged-S*, Dodd, Mead, 1938.

was hired to build the plane for this flight, and he added a third engine in the nose and enlarged its fuel tanks. "New York - Paris" was optimistically painted on the fuselage, and most experts believed his plane would win the prize.

Tragically, a few months after Charlie's visit, the plane's undercarriage broke during take-off, and the fuel-laden S-35 crashed and exploded. The pilot and co-pilot managed to crawl to safety, but the engineer and radio operator were stationed in the rear of the plane and perished in the flames.

Charlie's next destination was considerably more ambitious: the Boeing Airplane Company in Seattle.[58] Getting there would require a 3500-mile trek, across a foreign country, by himself.

In those days, a motorcycle trip from the east coast to the west coast would have been nearly impossible, if it were not for the Yellowstone Trail. It was a telling example of American culture that one of the first transcontinental roads was created by a grass-roots movement of private citizens, with neither help nor hindrance from the federal government.[59] An association of automobile and motorcycling enthusiasts joined forces with businessmen and town officials, who recognized the opportunity for tourism and commerce. With their organization, a series of interconnecting roads were upgraded or created, until it was possible to drive from Plymouth Rock to Puget Sound. The project began in 1912, and by the time Charlie made his trip, it was a well-established operation, with maps, gas stations, restaurants and hotels along the way. And if anyone did get lost, there was an iconic yellow disk with a black arrow painted on rocks and trees along the way.

The trip began on July 24, 1926, but it almost came to an end on the first day. In Albany, a woman driving a Ford ran into Charlie's motorcycle. Luckily, neither he nor his cycle was badly damaged. The cycle could go about 150 miles on a tank of gas, and that was a good day's journey from one town to the next. Some nights, he saved money by sleeping in an old tent. As an explorer, nature enthusiast and amateur botanist, he enjoyed the trip through a broad spectrum of terrains and climates. He was even more

---

[57] The Curtiss NC-4 had crossed the Atlantic in 1919, flying from Newfoundland to Lisbon, but it made a mid-Atlantic refueling stop at the Azores. A month later, A British Vickers Vimy aircraft crossed nonstop from Newfoundland to Ireland. Nevertheless, the Orteig Prize seemed to capture the public imagination more dramatically.

[58] Personal communication with Newell Bossart and Karel Jan Bossart Jr. 2012.; Smith, Ernest N., "Shrinking the Continent," *American Motorist* magazine, December 1925.; Brahams, Dr. Harry G., Funeral eulogy for Karel Jan Bossart, La Jolla Presbyterian Church, August 5, 1975.; "De man die in Amerika aan het hoofd staat van de proefnemingen met de Atlasraket is een Antwerpenaar!," Flemish newspaper clipping from late 1958 or early 1959.

[59] Ridge, Alice A., John Wn. Ridge, *The Yellowstone Trail: A Good Road from Plymouth Rock to Puget Sound*, 2000.

interested in America's cities and people, and he made an effort to meet a variety of citizens in the cafes and hotels along the way. He wrote weekly letters to his parents, detailing his impressions, mishaps, and interesting people he met. His friend Jan Van Overloop read the letters too, and later described them as the best stories he ever read about the United States.[60]

The first half of the trip took him through rich farmland and the industrial cities of the East: Buffalo, Cleveland, Toledo, Chicago, Milwaukee and Minneapolis. Beyond there, he entered the American West, through the picturesque badlands of South Dakota and into Montana, where the roads were mostly unpaved. More than once, his rickety motorcycle broke down in remote locations. On one occasion, an engine valve failed, and he improvised a temporary repair with string and a pine cone.

One of his favorite stops was Butte, Montana. For a student of mining engineering, there could be no more interesting place than "The Richest Hill on Earth." Gold, silver and gems had been mined there since the 1860s, but the real treasure was copper, an indispensable metal in the age of electricity. In 1882 miners discovered a 90-foot thick vein of Chalcocite, a lustrous high-grade copper ore. And that was only a taste of what lay below. By the time Charlie visited, Anaconda Copper Mining Company was the fourth largest corporation in the world. Underneath the city lay a 10,000-mile maze of shafts and tunnels. Outside of town, massive smelting operations belched smoke, devastating the vegetation for miles around.

Charlie felt right at home in Butte, which was not a typical western cowboy town. The people dressed in the latest fashions and read East-Coast newspapers. Theaters, gambling halls and saloons were open 24 hours a day. The young visitor befriended some of the rough working class folks and got a tour of the copper mining operation. Hanging around with the miners, he likely heard some of the local politics. Only a few years before, the radical union Industrial Workers of the World had staged a strike and the Army had to patrol the streets to quell violence.

Continuing west on the journey, the Pipestone Pass in Montana took him over the continental divide, then Blewett Pass crossed the Cascades, and a red brick road (which still exists) descended into Seattle. Like Antwerp, Seattle was a major ocean port located far inland, connected to the sea by a system of deep natural waterways. One of the first engineering attractions Charlie visited was the Smith Tower, a 42-story sky scraper, which was the tallest building in the western United States.

---

[60] Unfortunately, Charlie's letters home cannot be found now, but there are third-hand reports of the contents.

The primary objective of his trip was Boeing's aircraft plant. William Boeing had moved to Seattle to build a timber company, but he became fascinated by airplanes. He flew for the first time in 1910, sitting on the wing of a biplane at an exhibition. He learned to fly and bought his own plane, but in 1916 he decided he could design a better one himself. His company had close ties to MIT's aeronautics department, which may be how Charlie got the idea to visit. Their chief engineer, Wong Tsu, was one of the first graduates of the aeronautics program. Boeing's corporate co-founder, George Westervelt, was also an MIT graduate; and MIT helped the company build its first wind tunnel.

Boeing Plant No. 1 was a red barn-like building on the Duwamish River, originally a boat factory. The two-story structure was filled with wood-working tools powered by an overhead system of power shafts and belt drives.[61] Much of the company's income was from a contract with the Army Air Service for PW-9 biplanes. Inspired by the Fokker D.VII fighter used by Germany, Boeing designed steel tubular frameworks for the fuselages, fabricated with an arc-welding process they specially developed. The wing ribs and spar (the main support beam that runs through the length of the wing) were made from spruce, and the skin of the aircraft was canvas, cut and sewn together by teams of women.[62]

It was not an easy time to be in this business. After the First World War; demand for new aircraft plummeted, because the market was flooded with cheap military surplus planes. Airplanes were still too small and uncomfortable to support a thriving passenger-plane industry. Once again, Herbert Hoover had an indirect impact on Charlie's career. As Secretary of Commerce from 1921-1928, Hoover believed in the economic benefits of new technology such as radio and aviation. He promoted the idea that air mail service would stimulate the aircraft industry, and he also believed it would stimulate the economy in general, by increasing the rate of information exchange. In 1925, Congress passed the Airmail Act, allowing the postal service to contract with private airlines. Boeing took advantage of this new market by building a specialized airmail plane, the Model 40.

A dozen aircraft makers were in the business of making mail planes, but one of the most reliable and lucrative was built by Ryan Airlines, Inc. To visit them, Charlie motorcycled from Seattle to San Diego down the Pacific Highway, another grass-roots automobile trail and one of the longest asphalt-paved roads in the world at the time.

---

[61] The structure was moved and restored at Boeing's Museum of Flight, filled with photographs from the era when Charlie visited.

[62] "William E. Boeing – 1881 to 1956," www.boeing.com.

T. Claude Ryan and his partner B.F. Mahoney had several businesses: a flight school, a passenger service between San Diego and Los Angeles, and the manufacture of mail planes. Their factory was a former fish cannery on Harbor Street, a building in poor condition with many of the window panes broken. Like Boeing's planes, Ryan's M-1 and M-2 mail carriers were based on concepts from the Fokker D.VII. A fuselage of tubular steel was built on the ground floor of the plant, and wings supported by a wooden spar were constructed in the loft. The building was permeated with the smell of silver butyrate, aluminum powder and celluloid dissolved in banana oil.[63] This sealed and protected the cloth hull against moisture and solar ultraviolet rays. Completed bodies and wings were driven to the company hangar at the Dutch Flats Airport, for final assembly.

The year after Charlie's visit, Ryan Airlines became more famous, when Charles Lindbergh hired them to build a special plane. They redesigned an M-2, with a wider wingspan and a giant fuel tank. With the "The Spirit of St. Louis," Lindbergh flew from New York City to Paris in 1927, winning the Orteig Prize.

After seeing Ryan's operation, Charlie was out of money and stuck in southern California. He had to get back to MIT for the start of the 1926 fall term and was forced to sell his watch and motorcycle to buy passage: a train to New Orleans and a steamship to New York City. Once in New York, he could get his cash allowance from the Belgian Consulate. He barely had enough to purchase the tickets, and during the three-day layover in Louisiana, he was penniless and hungry. Since meals were included in his ticket, as soon as he got onboard the ship, the young man ate everything in sight.[64]

In their final term, graduate students and aeronautics majors did a thesis project. In the early days of the department, the topics were usually perfunctory exercises suggested by the faculty advisor, such as measuring the take-off distances of airplanes, the strength of welded joints, torsion stresses on a wing, etc. However, Charlie chose to work on the kite-ship invention he had patented in Belgium. In his thesis, he did a more complete mathematical analysis, and he estimated that his sailboat could reach a speed of 70 mph tacking in a 15 mph wind.[65]

On June 7, 1927, a Master of Science degree in Aeronautical Engineering was awarded to Charles J. Bossart.

---

[63] Lindbergh, Charles A., *The Spirit of St. Louis*, Scribners, 1953.

[64] Mary Bossart-Halfpenny, school paper on her grandfather based on interviews with Dora Bossart Scott and other family members, in 1984.; Dora's letter to Mary, March 14, 1984.

[65] Bossart, Charles J., *Sailing flight. Description and discussion of a new method of motorless flying*, Thesis (M.S.)--MIT, Dept. of Aeronautical Engineering, 1927.

While Charlie was completing his master's degree, he could not have guessed that he was studying only 40 miles from an event that would be significant to his eventual career in rocket design. On March 16, 1926, a physics professor named Robert Goddard launched the world's first liquid-fuel rocket. Powered by gasoline and liquid oxygen, the ten-pound rocket flew to a height of only 41 feet and came down 184 feet from the launch pad. Not an impressive flight, but it was the beginning of a series of increasingly more sophisticated experiments in the following years.[66]

The concept of the liquid-fuel rocket was first discovered in the 1890s and published in 1903, by an eccentric Russian school teacher named Konstantin Tsiolkovsky.[67] Space rockets had appeared in science fiction, but Tsiolkovsky was the first to analyze the problem scientifically, with a mathematical formula for rocket performance. Was it possible to reach outer space using chemical energy? The answer was yes…but just barely. He realized that contemporary black-powder rockets were not capable of achieving space-travel velocity. To achieve the necessary rocket speed, he hit upon the new idea of powering the engine with high-energy liquid propellants: specifically, liquid oxygen and liquid hydrogen.

In the west, Tsiolkovsky's writings were not discovered until the late 1920s. Prof. Goddard independently derived the same formula for rocket velocity, and he patented the liquid-fuel rocket in 1914. Unlike Tsiolkovsky, Goddard had been concerned with making rockets lighter-weight to get the necessary speed. In a solid-fuel rocket, he noted that the entire body had to be strong enough to contain the pressure of combustion. He reasoned that liquid fuel could be fed into a small heavy-duty combustion chamber, and the rest of the rocket structure only had to be strong enough to hold the fuel and survive the stress of flight.

In 1920 Goddard wrote an influential paper on his theory of rockets and described experiments he had performed. At the end of the paper, he discussed the possibility of building a rocket that could impact the Moon. The Moon-rocket idea was met with world-wide interest, but it was denounced as scientifically impossible in the New York Times.[68] Upset by the negative publicity, and paranoid about people stealing his ideas, Goddard's subsequent work was cloaked in secrecy.

In 1930, with funding from the Smithsonian Institution and the Guggenheim family, he moved operations from his aunt's farm in Auburn,

---

[66] Goddard, Esther, Pendray G. Edward, *The Papers of Robert H. Goddard*, McGraw Hill, 1970.

[67] Tikhonravov, M.K., *K.E. Tsiolkovsky: Trudy Po Raketnoi Tekhnike*, Oborongiz, Moscow 1947.

[68] "A Severe Strain on Credulity," *New York Times*, Jan 13, 1920.

Massachusetts to a safer and more private location near Roswell, New Mexico. By 1932, he was launching large rockets with gyroscopic guidance systems, and the sophistication of his work was not surpassed by anyone until German experiments in the late 1930s.[69]

On returning to Belgium, Charlie served a year of mandatory military service, as a sergeant in the 3rd Corps of the *Aéronautique Militair*, the Belgian air force. In February of 1929, after his term of service was complete, he began working at Emile Allard's research institute, the *Service Technique de l'Aéronautique Belge* (STAé.), at Sint-Genesius-Rode.[70]

When the STAé was founded in 1922, its first major facility was a two-meter diameter wind tunnel of the open-return type (a straight tunnel that takes in fresh air at one end, as opposed to tunnels that recirculate air in a closed loop). Like the tunnels at MIT, a fan at the rear created suction, so air could enter the front and pass through the experimental area without turbulent backwash from the fan blades.

Originally founded to service the civil aviation authority, by the time Charlie started work, the STAé was a part of the Belgian Defense Ministry. After a probationary period as a trainee engineer (*ingenieur op de proef*), Charlie became a senior aerodynamics engineer (*hoofdingenieur*) on the two-meter tunnel, used to test and certify military aircraft.

MIT was a valuable experience, but in the early years of their program, as Charlie later said, "They didn't know very much about airplanes there."[71] However at the STAé., he was immersed in the more experienced European aircraft culture. The laboratory had strong ties to industry, and Allard and his colleague Alfred Renard designed and built working airplanes. The Russian expatriate Nicolas Florine[72] was also there, developing one of the world's first experimental helicopters.

But despite these interesting projects, two years spent in the United States had made a deep impression on Charlie and changed his expectations. He had seen more of America than most of its citizens do, and the freedom and opportunity of its society appealed to his free-thinking rational character. Unlike a comparable European journey, his motorcycle trip across thousands of miles did not require border crossings, identity papers or being stopped and questioned by suspicious police every time he passed through a town.

---

[69] Specifically, von Braun's A-3 test rocket launched in 1937.
[70] Today it is called the Von Kármán Institute for Fluid Dynamics.
[71] Interview of Mr. K.J. Bossart by John L. Sloop, April 27, 1974.
[72] Nikolai Anatolevich Florin.

In America, he became used to the friendly informality of society. If he made a mistake at MIT, someone would say, "Sorry Charlie, but you're wrong." However, at the STAé., the technicians and workmen under him never dared to talk back, even though he had far less real-life experience. If he made a suggestion, good or bad, the response was always a servile, "*Ja, meneer de ingenieur!*" ("Yes, Engineer Sir!").[73] They would never share their opinions and experience with him.

In America, Charlie saw a growing aviation industry and a chance to control his own destiny in a way that was difficult in the old world. He was not alone in thinking this, and many great European designers and engineers in the field, like Antony Fokker, were moving to the United States or opening branches of their aircraft companies there.

---

[73] De Bruyn, Frans, *De Klap Op De Vuurpijl*, Antwerp, 1964.

Karel's parents, Carolina Tyck and
Louis Bossart. Joanna Van Horenbeek
with grandson Karel. Early photograph
of Karel and his sister Dora. (*Courtesy of
the Scott Family*)

Karel Jan Bossart at age 16 (*Courtesy of Scott Family*).

The Free University of Brussels on Stuiver Street.

The 7.5-foot wind tunnel at MIT (*Courtesy of Technique, 1925*).

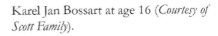

The ramparts and moat of Antwerp. German Zeppelin above the tower of Out Lady Cathedral.

The Bossart home in Kalmthout (*Courtesy of Dora Scott*).

2

Stress and Strain

After working for a year in Belgium, Charlie quit his job in February, 1930 and made plans to immigrate to the United States. He turned down a professorship in aerodynamics at Ghent University, which would have been a safe career choice.[74] But it was the new world that beckoned.

He told his sister, Goodbye, *Ik ga naar Amerika*! (I'm going to America) but his father was dismayed by the decision. Louis had built a small office addition to his home, for when his son returned from MIT, but sadly, it was never used. By then, the young man had made up his mind to set out on a more independent life, no longer controlled by his father or what he saw as the formality and conformity of Belgian society. In fact, he had applied for a visa to the United States in early January, where he had a job lined up as a stress analyst at Sikorsky Aircraft Corporation.

Igor Sikorsky was one of the greatest minds of aeronautics. Charlie's credentials could undoubtedly have found him work at any number of aircraft companies in the United States, but something about Sikorsky had made an impression on the young man. The son of a Russian professor, Sikorsky was an intellectual with broad knowledge of science, history, astronomy and theology. He was known for his charm and generosity to fellow refugees from the Soviet revolution. As an aircraft designer, he was a daring and creative genius, even mystical at times, with ideas sometimes coming to him in dreams. However, he insisted on checking his designs with mathematics and testing, rejecting even the most cherished idea if it proved wrong.[75] In the early days, airplanes were designed more by intuition, but Sikorsky was an early adopter of new scientific techniques.

---

[74] Interview with Dora Bossart Scott by Myrle Ann Bossart, 2000.

All of this made working for Sikorsky attractive, and to top it off, his company was embarking on a bold new project. He had recovered from the S-35 disaster, and was about to build the largest airplane in America.

His new career began with Charlie's arrival in New York City on April 12, 1930. This time, Herbert Hoover was not paying for the voyage, so he had booked cheap tickets on the cargo ship S.S. Carlier. In New York, Perrin C. Galpin (the head of Hoover's scholarship program) was kind enough to let him stay at his apartment for a few days. By May, he was settled into a rented room on 98 Margherita Lawn, in Stratford Connecticut, about a mile from work.[76] His landlord was Nick Glad,[77] one of Sikorsky's inner circle of refugee Russian engineers.

A lot had happened to Sikorsky and the aircraft industry since Charlie visited him in 1926. By 1930, the air-travel industry was beginning its rapid growth. A few years before, military contracts and airmail had sustained the market, but now the situation was changing, with the appearance of larger airplanes, comfortable closed cabins and a better public perception about air safety. Sikorsky had been close to bankruptcy after the fatal crash of the S-35, but his luck improved after he built the S-34 and S-36 experimental seaplanes. These flying boats gave him the opportunity to enter into a profitable relationship with Pan American Airways and realize his old dream of building large passenger planes.[78]

Established companies like Ford and Fokker already dominated production of the planes used for overland air routes granted to the "big four" airlines (Eastern, United, American and TWA). A fifth airline, Pan American, was given exclusive rights to over-water international routes (but barred from over-land business). Seaplanes were ideal, because they permitted immediate access to coastal areas where airports had not yet been built. Furthermore, many people believed they were fundamentally safer for long over-sea flights, because they could make emergency landings on water. For Sikorsky, seaplanes were ideal because their manufacture was an economic niche with few big competitors.

Beginning in 1927, Pan American began regular airmail and passenger flights between Florida and Cuba. The airline hired Charles Lindbergh as their technical advisor and test pilot, and Lindbergh formed a close friendship with Igor Sikorsky. The airline leased the S-36 prototype to explore possible new routes in South America and the Caribbean. They

[75] Sikorsky, Igor, *The Story of the Winged-S*, Dodd, Mead, 1938.
[76] *List or Manifest of Alien Passengers for the United States Immigration Officer at Port of Arrival*, New York, April 12, 1930.; *Fifteenth Census of the United States: 1930*.
[77] Nicholas Gladkevich (1900-1993).
[78] Sikorsky, Igor, *The Story of the Winged-S*, Dodd, Mead, 1938.

built and sold four S-36s, but it was the S-38 that became Sikorsky's first big success. The twin-engine S-38 had a 72-foot wingspan and first flew in 1928. The company eventually sold 114 of the eight-passenger amphibians. Pan American purchased 39 and used them to expand service to Caribbean islands and the Gulf Coast of Texas, Mexico and Central America.[79]

With the profits from the S-38 and money from investors, the Sikorsky Aviation Corporation was able to move out of leased factory space on Long Island and built a $5 million plant in Stratford, Connecticut. Located between the Avon Field airport and the mouth of the Housatonic River, it was close to the Long Island Sound and an ideal site for seaplane testing.[80] Operations at the plant began in the spring of 1929.

Charlie was assigned to the team building the largest seaplane yet: the S-40 amphibious passenger liner. Lindbergh and Pan American's chief engineer had worked with Sikorsky on the specification of this aircraft, capable of carrying 40 passengers. Sikorsky's proposal was a scaled up version of the S-38 with four Pratt & Whitney "Hornet" engines and a wingspan of 114 feet. But when Lindbergh first saw the design, he was unhappy with its aerodynamics—the large pontoons, uncowled engines, and wings reinforced by a forest of struts and cables, all of which would limit its speed and range. Sikorsky argued that they needed the experience of building this plane before they could safely design the next model, with the innovations that Lindbergh wanted.

Hired as a stress analyst, Charlie approached the subject with enthusiasm and creativity. He and his co-workers were to measure or calculate the weight and aerodynamic forces that act on the airplane, work out how those forces distribute throughout the structure, and verify that no part would be stressed to the breaking point. They considered the stresses of normal flying, turning, banking and the impact of landing; and they looked at loads generated by emergency maneuvers.

For seaplanes, they also had to study the hydrodynamic forces when the plane was moving on the water like a boat. They towed a test prototype on the river, attached by cable to a livestock scale, to measure the drag force.

This kind of analysis kept the aircraft as light as possible, by making parts strong enough but not unnecessarily massive. Sikorsky was an early adopter of this design methodology, and his stress-analysis reports ran to a thousand pages.[81]

---

[79] Allen, Roy, *The Pan Am Clipper*, Amber Books Ltd., 2000.
[80] Avon Field is today called the Igor I. Sikorsky Memorial Airport.
[81] Sikorsky, Igor, *The Story of the Winged-S*, Dodd, Mead, 1938.

Aircraft design required an understanding of material properties and how to manage the weight of structures (rocket design would someday push those requirements even further). Charlie was eager to tackle the challenge, and he devised a novel technique for analyzing the stress in the S-40 wing.[82] The wing structure was supported by front and rear box spars (hollow tubes of duralumin) and metal skin, all of which were load-bearing. Aft of the rear spar, the wing was skinned with fabric, to save weight. In Charlie's new technique, the total bending and shearing forces on the wing were first computed, and then individual stresses on the various parts (spars, ribs, skin) were found. The calculation of aerodynamic forces during flight were based on confidential studies done by the NACA and shared with American manufacturers.

For a better understanding of Charlie's part in this process, it is helpful to know a few basic concepts about stress analysis. While the quantitative mathematical calculations of stress analysis require advanced training, the concepts are straightforward.

The term *stress* refers to various types of force (pounds per square inch) acting on a given part of the plane; for example, pressure, tension or shearing. Stress originates from a number of sources: the weight of the structure, aerodynamic drag during flight, the lift of the wings, the thrust of the engine and inertial forces generated by turns and acceleration.

With stress comes *strain*, which refers to the deformation of a material in response to stress; for example, stretching, bending or twisting. The flexibility of a material is indicated by the stress-to-strain ratio, the so-called *Young's modulus*. A low value indicates a very elastic material, and a high value indicates a rigid material. The most important task of the stress analyst is to verify that no part of the structure will be strained to the point of being permanently bent or failing. A commonly used strength measurement of a material is its *tensile strength*, the amount of stress required to pull it apart.

---

[82] Bossart, K., *A New and Very Ingenious Method for Structure Analysis of Box Spars*, Sikorsky Aircraft.; Bossart, K.J., *Method of Structural Analysis of a Monocoque Wing*, Sikorsky Aircraft.

Material[83]	Density	Tensile Strength	Strength to Weight Ratio	Young's Modulus
Spruce	0.43	86	200	10
Duralumin	2.78	483	174	73
Stainless 301	7.88	1276	162	183
Magnesium	1.79	260	145	42
Aluminum 6061	2.70	310	115	69

Both the strength and weight of a material have to be taken into account when evaluating a material. For example, spruce, a common wood used in airplanes, is not as strong as steel, but it is much lighter. Thus, a thick spruce beam could have the same weight and strength as a hollow steel tube. This idea is quantified by the *strength-to-weight ratio*.[84] Spruce has a higher ratio than duralumin and some steel alloys, but wood has the disadvantage of being very flexible, as its low Young's modulus indicates.

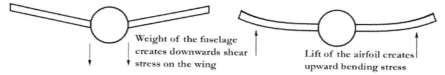

Weight of the fuselage creates downwards shear stress on the wing

Lift of the airfoil creates upward bending stress

The first step for the stress analyst is to consider the nominal stress of an aircraft in level flight at normal cruise speed. The thrust of the engine propels the airplane, pulling it through the air and creating stress on the engine mounts. The most critical stress is produced in the wings. During flight, two important types of wing stress must be analyzed. First, where the wings join the fuselage, the weight of the aircraft pulls down on the wing, creating a shearing force. In addition, the lift of the airfoil generates a force distributed across the wing that tries to bend it upward.

Level flight at cruise velocity is not the most demanding situation that can occur. An airplane can fly into turbulence, make a hard turn, pull out of a dive or even fly upside down. To design a safe aircraft, circumstances that create extraordinary stress must be considered, but it is not practical to analyze all of these special circumstances or to anticipate them all. Instead, aircraft designers take the nominal stress of level flight and multiply it by a safety margin called a *load factor*, designing the parts to withstand the larger stress. Choosing load factors was something of an art, based on years of

---

[83] The Atlas was built from Stainless Steel 301, and the MX-774-B was built from 6061. Their quirks will be discussed in later chapters. The numbers in this table are modern metric values.

[84] Strictly speaking, it is the tensile strength to density ratio.

experience, and some values were mandated by law. Load factors of six or seven were typical.[85]

Understanding the properties of materials is another important part of aircraft design and stress analysis. Charlie was starting out at a particularly interesting time for an aeronautical engineer, when metals were replacing wood as the primary material in aircraft. As new metal alloys were being invented, airplane designers had to work around some of their problematic issues. An example of this quirkiness was duralumin, the most popular metal used for aircraft. When that aluminum alloy was first produced experimentally, its strength was not impressive. But when a sample was tested a few days later, it was found to have "age hardened" into a remarkably strong metal. Unfortunately, duralumin's hardness was easily destroyed by heat, so it could not be welded. Instead, rivets had to be used to fabricate structures from sheets and tubes of duralumin.

New materials were not the only technology driving airplane design. The 1930s also saw a "structural revolution" in aircraft.[86] In biplanes, rigidity had been obtained by a system of triangles formed by struts and cables, in essence, a truss between the upper and lower wings that stopped the whole assembly from bending, shearing or twisting. But the biplane was being supplanted by a new design: the *cantilever wing*. These were supported by an internal beam (the spar), instead of external wires and braces. Pioneered by the Dutch aircraft designer Anthony Fokker, the cantilever wing ushered in the age of the monoplanes, which were lighter and more efficient than biplanes.

When Sikorsky came to America, he began to build aircraft from duralumin, starting with the S-29A. But while it was state of the art in using all metal, the structural design of the S-29A was a biplane, and his subsequent airplanes evolved in stages towards a more modern form. The S-38 was called a *sesquiplane*, because the lower wing was half the span of the 72-foot upper wing. It served largely as an anchor for the truss of struts that supported the main wing and the two engines. The S-40 was a true monoplane with a 114-foot span and four engines, but it still had horizontal booms extending from the fuselage, to anchor wing struts. This was a so-called *semi-cantilever* wing, because it was supported by both an internal spar and an external truss. Charlie understood the special mathematical technique for analyzing complex structures like trusses, the "method of least work," where the potential energy of the structure, when it was relaxed

[85] Pippard, A.J. Sutton, Capt. J. L. Pritchard, *Aeroplane Structures*, Longmans, Green & Co., 1919.
[86] Jakab, Peter L., "Wood to Metal: The Structural Origins of the Modern Airplane," *J. Aircraft*, 6, 1999.

in a state of equilibrium, was calculated to find the forces on each cable and strut.[87]

Another important concept in the "structural revolution" would also prove important in rocket design: the stressed-skin *monocoque fuselage*. Early aircraft bodies were built as a framework of longitudinal rails and bulkheads, covered with fabric or thin plywood skin. In 1911, the Swiss boat engineer Emile Ruchonnet was the first to experiment with airplane bodies that had no framework, and used only the skin to form a rigid tube. A load-bearing skin was a sophisticated technique for light-weight design that distributed load evenly throughout the surface. Sikorsky was the first aircraft designer to build a monocoque aircraft in Russia, in 1913 (the S-9), so he was well aware of the concept. However, his large seaplanes were *semi-monocoque*, a compromise that gave the best strength to weight ratio. This used a load-bearing skin augmented with a light framework, which is typical of modern airliners today.

Design work on the S-40 had begun a couple years before Charlie joined the company, but he was there in April of 1931, when it made its first test flight on the Housatonic River. Three of the airplanes were built, and Pan American named them "Clippers," after the famous sailing ships that pioneered commercial transport in the 19th century. The airline used the new planes to extend its routes to encircle the coast of South America, as far south as Buenos Aires and Santiago.

In his spare time, Charlie worked on a pet project with seasoned Sikorsky engineer Boris "Bob" Labensky. That summer, Bob, Charlie and another engineer, Robert Octavec, had an idea while they were relaxing on the Connecticut beach: a glider towed by a remote-controlled boat. In a sense, it was the opposite of Charlie's kite-ship invention. They built a light-weight biplane glider with a 30-foot wing span and a seaplane hull.

With three Sikorsky engineers doing the design, it was more sophisticated than a typical hobbyist's glider. It had a hull made from hyblum (a stainless aluminum-nickel-chromium alloy), and chromium-molybdenum steel tubing was used for the framework. It was connected by a steel cable to a 32 horsepower unmanned motor boat that could be remote controlled by wire from the glider cockpit. Wires taped to the cable controlled relays to steer left or right, advance or retard the throttle, and start and stop the engine. Labensky was the only trained pilot in the group, but Charlie and Robert learned to fly it up and down the beach at an altitude of 200 to 400 feet.[88]

---

[87] Pippard, A.J. Sutton, Capt. J. L. Pritchard, *Aeroplane Structures*, Longmans, Green & Co., 1919.

Charlie found America in the 1930s much changed from the economic boom times he experienced during his school days at MIT. In 1929 the stock market had crashed, banks failed, consumer spending contracted and unemployment exceeded 20 percent. For his humanitarian works, Herbert Hoover had been one of the most admired men in the world, but after he was elected President, the Great Depression tarnished his reputation forever. In the first few years of the Depression, Sikorsky's company lost money, but despite pressure from investors, Igor Sikorsky refused to lay off any of his loyal workers. In his mind, the stock market crash was a minor inconvenience compared to the trauma of the Russian communist revolution.[89]

For professional engineers in an emerging industry like aeronautics, employment and a steady salary were not problems. The Depression had caused prices to collapse by 33 percent, and in that deflated economy, Charlie and his friends enjoyed a lifestyle that was sometimes frivolous and whimsical.[90] Charlie was popular with the ladies, whom he courted with extravagance. He had a flamboyant affair with a Russian Countess and showered her with presents and attention. When she took a trip to Europe, he had her steamship stateroom filled with flowers.

In June, after a busy year with Sikorsky, Charlie had an unexpected career change. Sikorsky's old family friend and fellow aircraft designer, Alexander de Seversky,[91] was starting a new company to build his dream airplane. It was Seversky who had helped Sikorsky find his first job when he arrived in America. In 1930, working on commission, Seversky had helped sell S-38 seaplanes. So when he asked for advice finding a chief engineer, Sikorsky was happy to help, and with work on the S-40 complete, he recommended Charlie Bossart.

Like many Russian expatriates whom Charlie encountered, Seversky was a colorful character. During the First World War, he was a heroic pilot and lost a leg when the Germans shot down his plane. Shortly after the communist revolution, Seversky had been sent to the United States on official business, and as a member of the nobility, he decided it was unsafe to return to Russia. He worked with Sperry Corporation to develop the first gyroscopically stabilized bombsight, and he helped the Army Air Service develop in-air refueling techniques.

---

[88] "Build This Self-Towing Seaplane Glider Now," *Mechanics and Handcraft*, Spring, 1934.

[89] Delear, Frank J., *Igor Sikorsky: His Three Careers in Aviation*, Dodd, Mead & Co. 1969.

[90] Mary Bossart-Halfpenny, biography of her grandfather based on interviews with Dora Bossart Scott and other family members, in 1984.

[91] Alexander Nikolaievich Prokofiev de Seversky (1894-1974).

After the First World War, the U.S. Navy obtained funding for a series of giant battleships, which they argued were undefeatable. An outspoken proponent of the Air Service, General Billy Mitchell bragged that aircraft could sink any battleship and money would be better spent building a fleet of fighter planes. In February of 1921, the Navy reluctantly agreed to a demonstration of aerial bombing, using a captured German battleship as the target. Seversky was a friend of Mitchell's, and he advised him to drop the bombs, not directly on the ship, but in the water next to it, where the water-hammer effect would cave in the the hull. It was a trick he had used in the war.[92] When Mitchell's planes sunk the battleship, it was a major publicity triumph for the Air Service, and the Navy was humiliated and outraged.

Seversky's original company, which sold aircraft parts and instruments, went bankrupt in the Depression. But with new financing he formed a second company in February, 1931. He set up headquarters on Lexington Avenue in New York City, with just a draftsman, a secretary and one engineer. Seversky was planning the highly innovative SEV-3 all-metal amphibian plane. Sikorsky's planes were "flying boats," which landed on a boat-like hull, but Seversky's aircraft was a "float plane," which was more like a conventional airplane with pontoons in the place of wheels for its landing gear.

The fuselage of the SEV-3 would be a stressed-skin monocoque design with no internal framework. Further weight was saved by omitting fuel tanks inside the wings and using the sealed metal skin of the wing itself as the fuel container. This technique was called a "wet-wing." These were state of the art concepts in aircraft design.

It was a fascinating project, but Charlie's situation was not yet settled. A few months before Seversky hired him, a notorious aviation disaster started a chain of events that would change everyone's plans. On the morning of March 31, 1931, TWA flight 599 crashed, while flying through bad weather over Kansas. All six passengers and two crewmen perished, including the famous and beloved football coach of Notre Dame University, Knute Rockne. They were flying in an F-10 Fokker trimotor, one of the most successful passenger planes of the time. It was obviously a structural failure; one wing had broken off and fell half a mile from the main crash site.[93]

The public demanded information, and the usual attempts to hush it up or apply spin control were futile. Prior to this, it was not unusual for an airline to quietly clean up a crash site even before federal investigators

[92] Libbey, James K., *Alexander P. de Seversky and the Quest for Air Power*, Potomac, 2013.
[93] Friedman, Herbert M., "The Legacy of the Rockne Crash," *Aeroplane Magazine*, May 2001.

arrived. But eventually, the Department of Commerce discovered that the wooden box spar had broken. Moisture buildup had dissolved the glue holding the plywood together, causing the hollow beam to delaminate. As a result of this accident, wooden spars were outlawed in passenger planes, and TWA went so far as to publicly burn some of its F-10 fleet. Anthony Fokker was scandalized and returned to The Netherlands to start a new company. At that time, the major auto makers were involved in the aircraft business, and General Motors owned 40 percent of Fokker's aircraft company. Now Fokker was forced to resign and sell his remaining shares to GM. The company was renamed General Aviation Manufacturing Corporation, to escape the stigma of its former name.[94]

One consequence of this corporate shake-up at Fokker was the resignation of his star engineer, Alexander Kartveli. Seversky had been trying for years to hire him, and now Kartveli agreed to join the new company. After Charlie had worked only three weeks as chief engineer, Seversky gave him the bad news, "Sorry about this Bossart, but I can only afford one engineer." Luckily, Charlie was able to trade places with Kartveli, taking a job at General Aviation.[95]

In August of 1931, Charlie started work at the former Fokker plant in Hasbrouck Heights, New Jersey, now General Aviation's factory. A month later, they closed the New Jersey and West Virginia facilities and consolidated operations at Dundalk, Maryland, a suburb of Baltimore. They set up shop in a 200,000-square-foot factory next to Logan Field airport, leased from the Curtiss-Caproni Company.[96] Here, the young engineer was finally able to settle into a job. The only major project under development that year was a large search-and-rescue seaplane commissioned by the U.S. Coast Guard. It is not known what Charlie's first work assignment was, but the amphibian would have been well suited to his experience with seaplanes at Sikorsky.

Charlie's biggest job at General Aviation was on an aircraft that is something of a mystery today. In an interview he stated that he worked on a trimotor passenger plane in competition with the Douglas DC-2.[97] But what was that aircraft?

[94] More precisely, GM created a holding company called General Aviation Corporation, and GAC owned the manufacturing company GAMC, as well as other holdings.
[95] Sloop, John L., *Interview of Mr. K.J. Bossart*, NASA, April 27, 1974.; Bossart, Karel Jan, DA Form 643A, *Personal History Statement*, June 1, 1950.
[96] Preston, Lanman, and Breilhan, *Maryland Aloft*, Maryland Historical Trust, 2003.
[97] Shearer, Lloyd, "Charlie Bossart, Father of the Atlas," *Parade*, March 1, 1959.

In the aftermath of the F-10 crash, the public perceived wooden aircraft to be unsafe, and the government mandated expensive inspection protocols for them. TWA had a fleet of aging Fokker F-10s, and they desperately needed a more modern replacement. The Boeing 247 was under development (considered by experts to be the first truly modern airliner), but United Airlines had negotiated an exclusive deal to buy the first 60 of them. In August, 1932, TWA sent a letter of request to several other aircraft manufacturers. It specified an all-metal trimotor monoplane, capable of carrying 12 passengers, and the airline promised to buy at least 10 planes. The historic Douglas DC-2 airliner came from this request, but General Aviation also took up the challenge to meet TWA's specifications.

The next month, General Aviation bought the plans and patents for a single-engine passenger plane designed at Fairchild. GA's engineers worked quickly, replacing the cloth-on-metal framework with an all-metal design, skinned with duralumin. In January of 1933, the ten-passenger GA-43 made its first test flight, but this plane did not meet the requirements of TWA. At the same time, Charlie was assigned to a team that enlarged the design into a 16-passenger trimotor. In February, General Aviation announced plans for the not-yet-built trimotor GA-38.[98]

While design and stress analysis of the trimotor proceeded, corporate strategies were in the works. In January, GM announced their plan to purchase a controlling interest in North American Aviation,[99] a holding company that owned TWA, Eastern Airlines, Douglas, Sperry Gyroscope, Berliner-Joyce, Curtiss-Wright and others. This created a dilemma for General Motors, because now they owned both the GA-38 and DC-2 projects. GM assigned one of its brightest executives and troubleshooters, Ernest Breech, to oversee this new investment and act as chairman of North American Aviation.

On February 21, Breech met with TWA's technical consultant Charles Lindbergh. With Lindbergh at the controls of a small airmail plane and the GM vice president curled up in the mail compartment, they flew from New York City to Dundalk to review the GA-38. Breech favored the twin-engine DC-2, but Lindbergh endorsed the GA-38, because he thought trimotors were inherently safer in case of an engine failure. In the summer of 1933,

---

[98] Boyne, Col. Walter J., "General Aviation Gamble: the GA-43," *The Surly Bonds of Earth*, September 24, 2011 (air-boyne.com).; Allen, Richard S., "General Aviation's Clark GA-43," *Skyways*, January, 1998.; *General Motors World*, July 1933.

[99] *Annual Report to Stockholders*, North American Aviation, Inc., 1933.; The deal, approved by shareholders in April, was typically complicated: GM's subsidiary holding company GAC sold GAMC to NAA in exchange for 43.26% of its stock. GM then bought 8.74% of NAA on the open market. As chairman, Breech converted NAA from a holding company into a manufacturing company.

illustrations of both the DC-2 and the GA-38 appeared in trade magazines, with the TWA logo on their side. Work was allowed to continue on the trimotor, and now that GAMC and NAA were combined, General Aviation moved its operation to the Berliner-Joyce factory, on the other side of the airport from their old location. This meant access to a new toy for Charlie and the designers: Berliner-Joyce had one of the few large privately-owned wind tunnels in the world.[100]

In the meantime, when he was not at work, Charlie spent time sailing on Chesapeake Bay. His sailing buddies included Dudley Chase and an engineer he had known at Sikorsky named Clete Baum, now working at Berliner-Joyce.[101] Charlie was between girlfriends when Clete suggested, "Go over to the Chases' and take a look, they have four gals."[102] He was referring to the family of Dudley's uncle, Newell Dixon Chase, a civil engineer for the city of Baltimore.

Newell had four daughters. The youngest, Marion, was already dating someone, and the oldest daughter Katherine was married and moving to California. Charlie dated Sarah Chase for a time, but they broke up, and she later married his friend Clete. Shortly after this, Charlie met Cornelia, the fourth Chase sister, at a party thrown by Dudley.[103] Cornelia, or "Connie" as her friends called her, was well educated, with a degree in chemistry from Goucher College and a master's degree in psychiatric social work from Smith College. Starting a job as a family guidance counselor, she had just moved to Richmond, Virginia.

Connie was a kindred spirit with Charlie, an independent, confident woman who owned her own car and drove it at break-neck speed. The couple began a whirlwind romance. With prohibition still in force, Connie applied her knowledge of chemistry to the production of "bathtub gin" for the frequent parties they threw. Charlie began spending weekends in Richmond, unchaperoned visits that some conservative folks of that time did not approve of. On one occasion, seeing him step out to pick up the morning newspaper, a nosy neighbor called the vice squad.

In October of 1933, Charlie took a six-month leave of absence to visit Belgium. He had not seen his family for three years and decided to keep his trip a surprise. Dora did not know her brother was coming until he tapped on the window of their home in Kalmthout, and his father was surprised to find his son when he came into the kitchen chasing a fly with a swatter.[104]

[100] "New of the Month," *Flying Magazine*, May, 1930.
[101] Cleophas Philemon Baum (1906-1992).
[102] Virginia Baum Umberger, *personal communication*, 2013.
[103] Newell Chase, *personal communication*, 2012.

His Aunt Vire and her husband had just left their jobs with Red Star Line and built a hotel and restaurant they called "De Kievit" (the name of a local bird). Charlie was present for the inn's opening ceremony.[105]

When he was working at Sikorsky on the S-40, he was aware of a problem with its design called "porpoising." During landing, it sometimes pitched up and down violently enough to throw passengers out of their seats. In Antwerp, Charlie built a model seaplane he named "Zénobieke" (after Belgian electrical engineer, Zénobe Gramme, whom he especially admired). While Dora and her friend Mathilda took notes and piloted a motor boat on the river Scheldt, Charlie simulated take-offs and landings with the model on a pole, just as they tested seaplane hulls at Sikorsky.[106] It is possible that Charlie worked on this problem because he knew that the GA-38 was doomed and that he might resume work at Sikorsky.

Charlie returned to America in April of 1934. He went back to work in Dundalk, at the plant which was now officially part of North American Aviation. In June, the as yet nonexistent GA-38 was entered in a high-profile race from London to Melbourne, Australia.[107] However, before the race started in October, the trimotor was withdrawn, with an explanation that it would not be ready in time. As expected, the race was won by a de Havilland racing plane, specially designed for the event. But surprisingly, two all-metal airliners followed: a Douglas DC-2 came in second place and a Boeing 247 in third.

In fact, the GA-38 was probably cancelled by the time of the race. If there was any doubt about its fate, it was made clear by the appointment of "Dutch" Kindelberger as president of NAA, formerly the chief engineer at Douglas and head of the DC-2 project.[108] Furthermore, Kindelberger announced plans to move the Dundalk operation to Inglewood, California, where the climate was better suited for year-around aircraft testing. It was the right decision, because the DC-2 was a more streamlined, advanced aircraft, one of the great aeronautical engineering accomplishments of the time. But for Charlie, the plan to move the company away from the East Coast, where Connie's family lived, spelled the end of his employment at General Aviation.

---

[104] Dora Bossart Scott interviewed by Myrle Ann Bossart, 2000.
[105] Bastiaensen, Jean, "Kalmthout en de vader van de Atlasraket," *Tijdschrift van de Oudheidkundige Kring van Kalmthout*, No. 1, 2000.
[106] Verlinden, Gert, Obituary of Mathilda Van Hecke, 1955.
[107] "England-Australia Race," *Flight*, June 7, 1934.
[108] The DC-1 was a one-off experimental prototype for the DC-2.

In September, 1934, Charlie moved back to Stratford, Connecticut. With a substantial raise in salary, he started work on the structural analysis of the Sikorsky S-43 seaplane. The S-43 was called the "Baby Clipper," a scaled down version of Sikorsky's new S-42 "Clipper."

The S-42 was an aeronautical masterpiece, incorporating all the new technologies Sikorsky had hesitated to try in the S-40. While Douglas, Boeing and General Aviation were competing to build a 16-passenger airliner, Sikorsky was developing a plane that carried twice as many people and flew twice as far. The S-42 was state of the art: a streamlined design with true cantilevered wings, improved engines from Pratt & Whitney that were smoothly incorporated into the wing, and the efficient new Hamilton variable-pitch propeller (also used by Douglas in the DC-2). It was able to fly faster, farther and carry more than twice the payload of the S-40.

That November, Sikorsky was in London, where he deeply impressed the Royal Aeronautical Society with his presentation.[109] The speed and range of the S-42 was remarkable, but it was the high wing loading that surprised the audience (the ratio of airplane weight to wing area).[110] This allowed the S-42 to fly fast with a heavy payload, but it made it potentially impossible to take off or land at a safe speed. Sikorsky got around that problem in part by using the Hamilton propeller effectively, but his big innovation was a large flap on the wing that could be used to increase the wing area and lift during take-off and landing.

Ten of these giant planes were built, and Pan American bought them all. With a reduced payload, the S-42 was able to fly as far as 3000 miles, and this allowed the airline to reach Hawaii and extend its routes by island hopping all the way to Hong Kong and New Zealand.

Charlie worked on the S-43 which had half the capacity of the S-42. It had two engines instead of four, and an 86-foot wing containing a single spar (the S-42 had a span of 114 feet with two spars). The aircraft filled a market similar to the old S-38, and Sikorsky sold more than 50 of them. The millionaire Howard Hughes bought one for his personal use, but later crashed it in Lake Mead.

In June, 1935, an S-43 was ready for its first public flight. The plane they were testing had already been sold to Inter-Island Airways, in Hawaii, which would eventually buy four of the seaplanes. Sikorsky's engineering test pilot was Boris Sergievsky, who had been a flying ace in the anti-communist White Russian air force during the revolution. He had known

---

[109] Sikorsky, Igor I., *The S-42: The Development and Characteristics of a Long-Range Flying Boat*, Royal Aeronautical Society, London, November 15, 1934.

[110] Wing loads: S-42: 28.6, S-40: 18.1, Boeing 247: 16.3, Douglas DC-2: 19.7.

Sikorsky since their student days in Kiev Polytechnic Institute, and in the United States, Sergievsky had been working with Sikorsky since the design and construction of his first American airplane, the S-29A.[111]

As government observers, reporters and newsreel cameras looked on; Sergievsky powered up the engines and began to taxi down the Housatonic River and into Long Island Sound. Initially, the seaplane plowed through the water like a boat, and the engines had to work hard to overcome drag. When it gained enough speed, the craft began to hydroplane or travel "on the step." As it began to skim the waves, Sergievsky could feel something was wrong with one of the two engines. He reduced its power and skillfully adjusted the controls, making a perfect take-off. With just one engine working, he flew up and down the Sound and landed, showing no outward sign of trouble.

1936 began with a proud event. On February 5, Karel Jan Bossart completed the five-year residency requirement and became a naturalized citizen of the United States of America.

That August, his parents and sister arrived for a ten-week visit. Dora was completing a master's degree in physics at Ghent University, and both of his parents had retired from teaching. Charlie had just moved into an apartment in Sniffens Point, conveniently near the sailboat slips on the Housatonic River. He and Connie were still dating, and the Bossarts visited the Chase family in Baltimore.

The year ended with a change in Charlie's career. Soon after the S-43 was completed, Igor Sikorsky turned his attention from seaplanes to helicopters, which began a new era of innovations and success for the company. However, Charlie did not follow him into that new industry. A friend of Sikorsky from Russia was starting an experimental-helicopter company, and he asked Sikorsky to suggest an engineer. For a second time, he recommended Charlie Bossart.

That friend was Professor George de Bothezat, an aeronautics theorist who had won renown in Russia for work on the stability of aircraft and a theory of propellers.[112] Before the revolution, he had helped Sikorsky test aircraft designs in the wind tunnel of the St. Petersburg Polytechnic Institute. After the revolution, Bothezat immigrated to America, and in 1918 he was hired briefly to consult on research and wind tunnels for the Langley Laboratory of the NACA. The professor was not modest about his

[111] Sergievsky, Boris, *Airplanes, Women, and Song*, Syracuse University Press, 1999.
[112] Mikheev, V.R., *Georgy Aleksandrovich Botezat: 1882-1940*, Nauka, Moscow, 2000.; De Bothezat, George, *The General Theory of Blade Screws*, NACA report, 1920.

abilities, boasting "I am the world's greatest mathematician and scientist."[113] But he turned out to be all talk and no action. He not only did little to help the laboratory, but his arrogance and temperament alienated other scientists. The NACA had been warned that he was 'a brilliant mathematical physicist, but wholly untrustworthy', and they eventually dismissed him.[114]

In 1922, the U.S. Army funded his project to build a helicopter with four 8-foot rotors. It was required to reach an altitude of at least 25 feet during the tests. A rope of that length was tied to the landing strut, which it would have to lift entirely off the ground. However, it failed to rise more than six feet. After spending $200,000, a small fortune in those days, the Army cancelled the project. Bothezat later blamed the failure on sabotage, and among other things, he claimed a poisonous snake was sent in the mail in an attempt to assassinate him.[115] After the unsuccessful Army project, Bothezat formed a company, to apply his propeller theory to the design of high-efficiency fans. Among the projects done by his company was a unique vertical wind tunnel for the Sikorsky plant in Stratford.

Bothezat's new venture was called the Air-Screw Research Syndicate. The test pilot, Boris Sergievsky, was the vice president and financer of the company. Sergievsky had recently married into wealth, moved to his wife's mansion in the Adirondacks and now flew to the Sikorsky plant every day in his private plane. Charlie later joked, "Bothezat had a sugar daddy."[116]

Unaware of Bothezat's shaky reputation, Charlie was impressed by the professor and his plans. His new job as design engineer started in December of 1936, at a three-man office on 44th Street in Manhattan. Charlie worked with Bothezat and his special assistant, a former pilot in the Tsar's air force who styled himself Baron Vladimir Kuhn von Poushental. The Baron managed the office, drove the professor around and looked after his frail health. It was an unusual work environment, where the easiest way for them to communicate was for Charlie to speak French with Bothezat and English with von Poushental, while the Baron and the Professor spoke Russian.

The project was an outlandish one-man helicopter. It was to consist of a two-cylinder gasoline engine between two counter-rotating propellers, and the pilot would fly suspended below in a harness.[117] The whole machine would weigh about 75 lbs. and carry 20 lbs. of gasoline. It was a dangerous scheme; the pilot might break his legs landing too hard, and he would have

---

[113] Glines, C.V., "The Flying Octopus," *Air Force Magazine*, October 1990.
[114] Roland, Alex, *Model Research*, NASA History Series.
[115] Sergievsky, Boris, "Revealing a new Helicopter," *Mechanix Illustrated*, September, 1943.
[116] "Interview of Mr. K.J. Bossart by John L. Sloop," NASA, 1974.
[117] de Bothezat, George, "Helicopter Device," U.S. Patent 2,180,922, November 21, 1939.

to grab the engine when he touched down, or the whirling blades could strike the ground or fall on top of him. The design was soon improved so the pilot could sit in a chair that supported the engine. Years later, the original harness design was illustrated in a popular magazine, but it is unlikely that anyone ever tried to build it.[118]

Charlie worked on the project for two weeks. Each day the Baron told him how impressed they were with his work and his talent. Then one morning Bothezat summoned him to his apartment and said, "I'm not going to beat around the bush. You're no damn good, and you're fired!" [119]

After Charlie's departure, Bothezat's helicopter design evolved into a more practical one-man cabin with a tail: the GB-5. It was built and test flown by Sergievsky, but Bothezat never saw it completed. Suffering from a heart condition, the professor neglected his health until emergency surgery was required, and he passed away in 1940. Unfortunately, the GB-5 project never got far off the ground (literally) and the company soon failed.

Following his experience with the strange Professor de Bothezat, Charlie spent several months looking for work. In March of 1937, he found a position as stress analyst at Fleetwings Incorporated, a small aircraft company in Bristol, Pennsylvania. They owned a factory and docks on the Delaware River, where they developed small seaplanes. Their F-4 and F-5 Sea Birds were four-seat aircraft with a single engine above the wing. The Sea Birds were designed a few years earlier by James Reddig, whom Charlie knew from the MIT aeronautics program. The construction was a stainless steel framework covered with 10 mil (i.e., 10/1000 inch) stainless skin, only twice the thickness of a sheet of paper.[120]

These were some of the first planes to be built from stainless steel. The material was ideally suited to marine aircraft, where aluminum and structural steel were plagued by corrosion. Engineers at Fleetwings had become expert at the art of fabricating the material. Reddig joked, "they knew 18 different ways to weld a handle on a frying pan."

The process of welding stainless steel was tricky, and Fleetwings had licensed the technology from the Philadelphia company of E.G. Budd. Just three months after starting work as a stress analyst, Charlie got a better job offer from Budd: chief research engineer in the aircraft division.

---

[118] "One-Man Helicopters Give Soldiers Wings," *Popular Science*, March, 1940.

[119] Sloop, John L., *Interview of Mr. K.J. Bossart*, NASA, April 27, 1974.

[120] Baughman, Zachary, "Jim Reddig – An Insider's Look at the Design of the Fleetwings Sea Bird Amphibious Flying Boat," *Vintage Airplane*, August, 2004.; "A Shot-Welded Stainless Steel Amphibian," *Flight*, October 22, 1936.

Charlie began work for E.G. Budd in May of 1937. It was his introduction to the techniques of stainless steel, the alloy that would one day be used for Atlas. It was a material with remarkable properties but notoriously difficult to work with, and Budd's company was the first to master it.[121]

Stainless alloys of steel with chromium and nickel were studied by a number of companies around the turn of the century, most notably in Sheffield, England, where stainless steel kitchenware was first made. But it was the German steel and armament manufacturer Krupp that developed the highly successful 18-8 grade of steel (18% chromium, 8% nickel) in 1912. In the United States, Allegheny Steel Co. licensed 18-8 steel from Krupp, but, they were not sure if there would be a market for it. The new alloy cost 15 times as much as common structural steel, and although it was strong and corrosion-free, nobody knew how to fashion anything more complex than spoons and forks, which could be stamped out of sheets.

Every material had its quirks, but stainless steel had several. In its initial state, it had a tensile strength of 75,000 psi, but if it was cold rolled into sheets, it "work hardened," and its strength could increase to as high as 185,000 psi, three or four times as strong as ordinary carbon steel. There was a clear potential to build structures with much lighter weight, because less metal was needed to achieve the necessary strength.

But there was a problem. The heat from welding destroyed the metal's work-hardening, but even worse was the problem of "carbide precipitation," where the weld seam crystalized. Duralumin also had problems with welding, so aircraft were typically fabricated with rivets; however, this did not work for stainless steel. Drilling holes for rivets work hardened the metal until it became brittle or damaged the drill bit. Therefore, stainless steel had been little used after its invention.

Edward G. Budd began as an automobile maker, where he pioneered the use of stamped sheet metal and spot welding for assembly of all-steel car bodies. The process used high-amperage low-voltage electric current to melt the work piece by resistance. When Allegheny announced their stainless steel product, one of Budd's top engineers was intrigued and ordered some sheets. They quickly discovered that spot welding caused carbide precipitation. However, after many experiments they found that using brief bursts of power, 1/100th of a second, melted only a thin layer of metal at the face of contact. This produced a successful weld, without damaging the metal. They called the process "shot welding," and the patents gave Budd exclusive control over the fabrication of stainless steel.

[121] Biography of Karel J. Bossart, *High Altitude and Satellite Rockets, Cranfield Symposium*, July 18-20, 1957.

Their first idea for demonstrating shot-welding technology was an all stainless-steel airplane. After licensing the plans for a wooden seaplane from an Italian company, Budd's engineers carefully redesigned it using 18-8 alloy, skinning a metal frame with paper-thin sheets. The Budd BB-1 *Pioneer* first flew in the summer of 1932. It was as strong as the original wooden aircraft and even lighter weight. The prototype logged more than 1000 hours of flight in promotional tours in the U.S.A. and Europe, but they built only one and did not pursue aircraft any further at that time. In 1935, it was donated to the Franklin Institute, where it is still on display.[122]

The auto industry was not doing well during the Depression, and Budd decided to explore the application of stainless steel to passenger trains. In 1932, the president of Burlington Railway visited Budd and saw a demonstration of an experimental stainless-steel rail car. He was so impressed that he commissioned Budd to build a modern prototype train.

When it was completed two years later, the *Pioneer Zephyr* transformed the industry, and it excited renewed popular interest in rail travel. It was powered by a new kind of light-weight engine, using a diesel generator and electric motors. Diesel-electric technology rapidly replaced steam locomotive engines. Another innovation was the streamlined Art Deco design, which was not only beautiful, but it helped the trains to break speed records.[123]

Budd's engineers took full advantage of stainless steel's strength to build a structure considerably lighter than conventional steel. The entire three-unit *Pioneer Zephyr* weighed 97 tons, only a little more than a single standard Pullman passenger car. In one of Burlington's publicity events, ten men were able to pull the train on a level track. The structure was designed by Albert Dean, an aeronautical engineer who had graduated from MIT three years after Charlie. The all-stainless-steel train showcased Budd's shot-welding technique and employed classic aircraft design methodology. It was a semi-monocoque construction combining a light metal framework with a load-bearing skin of thin corrugated sheets.

After moving to Philadelphia in May, 1937, Charlie's first project with Budd was for a contract with the U.S. Army Air Corps. The Curtiss P-36 fighter was made from aluminum, a metal that could experience shortages during war time. So the Air Corps had asked Budd to create an experimental stainless-steel version of the P-36 wing. The challenge was to match or beat the weight and strength of the original.

---

[122] "Budd Pioneer X-749-N: Franklin Institute," B.R. Howard Assoc. 2008. (the company undertaking its restoration).

[123] "Edward Budd," *Streamliners: America's Lost Trains*, PBS, 2006.; Cobb, Harold M., *The History of Stainless Steel*, American Society for Metals, 2010.

Charlie's team included one of his best friends from Sikorsky, Bill Dieter, whom he hired in December.[124] Renato Contini, another aeronautical engineer, joined him from New York University. Several company personnel joined, bringing their experience from the Zephyr train project, including senior Budd engineer, John Whitesell.

The original Curtiss P-36 wing was state-of-the-art duralumin construction, fastened with rivets. The spar was an "I" beam, and the airfoil cross section was shaped by ribs made from sheets of metal, with holes punched out to lighten the structure. Finally, a load-bearing alclad skin was riveted to the ribs. The lift of the wing tended to bend it upward, and the bending force was resisted mostly by the horizontal caps at the top and bottom of the I-beam spar (compressing the upper cap and stretching the lower cap). Supporting the weight of the fuselage put a downward shearing force on the wing, and that was resisted by the vertical middle surface of the I-beam, the so-called "shear web."

Charlie's stainless-steel wing was constructed mostly from 8 mil sheets (0.008 inch). The design of the original aluminum wing could not be copied, because such thin stainless steel would buckle. Instead of an I-beam spar, he relied entirely on the corrugated skin of the wing to resist bending forces. A vertical shear web of corrugated stainless sheet ran the length of the wing. The skin was covered with a second smooth layer to reduce aerodynamic drag.[125]

The experimental stainless-steel wing was as light as the aluminum one, but it could not match the strength of the original P-36 wing. Charlie concluded that the problem with strength was caused by defective spot welds. With their pride in the shot-welding process, the management of Budd was not receptive to that report.[126]

While Charlie was living in Philadelphia, relations with Connie became more serious. He brought up the idea of getting married, but she was unsure. Connie decided she needed some time away from the situation and the pressure, and she signed up to spend the summer at a dude ranch in Wyoming. She asked her mother to keep her location a secret, but Charlie eventually found out and traveled out to the ranch. She was impressed by the effort he made to find her, and she was amused by his willingness to rough it in the country and ride a horse (which he did awkwardly).[127]

---

[124] Bill Dieter, personal notebook, scanned by his daughter, Betty Boyle.

[125] Bossart, Karel J., *et al, Airplane Wing*, U.S. Patent 2,275,038. Application 1938.

[126] Sloop, John L., *Interview of Mr. K.J. Bossart*, NASA, April 27, 1974.

[127] Cornelia Young, *personal communication*, 2013. (Katherine Chase's daughter).; Newell Bossart, *personal communication*, 2012.

Logical and free-thinking, he made it clear that she would not be trapped by the conservative divorce laws of that time, "If you don't like me, you can get out of the marriage any time." She finally said yes, but made it clear this would be the end of his reputation as a lady's man. It was the start of a long and successful partnership.

Cornelia Newell Chase and Karel Jan Bossart were married on September 24, 1938. The ceremony was held in the Chase family home in Cantonsville, Maryland. Charlie had been living in a boarding house in Philadelphia, but after their marriage, the couple moved into a rental home on West Penn Street. The next summer, they had their first child, a son named, Karel Jan Jr.

Charlie had become dissatisfied with E.G. Budd and resigned in December of 1939. His next job was assistant chief engineer at Spencer-Larsen Aircraft Corporation, in Amityville, Long Island. Charlie knew both the founders from when they worked with him on the Sikorsky S-43. Percival Spencer ("Spence" to his friends),[128] the company president, was the son of a famous inventor, and by the age of 17 he had built a steam-powered car and a working airplane. Victor Larsen,[129] the chief engineer, worked for Fokker and emigrated from Denmark to America in 1924. In 1937, they started a company together, working out of buildings on the site of the Kirkham Engineering Company in Farmingdale. They primarily sold airplane parts, but they soon began tinkering with an aircraft project.

In May of 1938, they completed a prototype: the SL-12C two-man seaplane. The most unique feature of the aircraft was a propeller mounted on a strut above and behind the cabin. Placing the propellers high was typical of seaplanes, to avoid spray during take-offs and landings. More unusual was that the four-cylinder engine was housed inside the cabin, rather than in a nacelle next to the propeller. That made the plane less top-heavy, but more mechanically complicated. From the engine, bevel gears linked to a vertical drive shaft that went up to the propeller strut, where another 90-degree turn was made by bevel gears to the propeller shaft.

In June, they made their first test flight, at Port Washington on the Long Island Sound. There were some issues with the hull and stall characteristics, but the biggest problem was torsional vibration in the vertical drive shaft. Usually the propeller of an aircraft is immediately next to the engine, mounted on the crank shaft. But in Larsen's design, play in

---

[128] Percival Hopkins Spencer (1897-1995), son of Christopher Miner Spencer.; Saevdal, Steinar, "Percival H. "Spence" Spencer," *Republic Seabee History*, www.seabee.info.
[129] Victor Aug Larsen (1902-1974).

the long drive train amplified piston impulses from the engine. This vibration was so severe that in 10 hours of test flying, they broke several drive shafts.[130]

Despite the difficulties, some of the shareholders were impressed enough to give them funding for the SL-15, a larger version with four seats. This was what allowed them to hire Charlie. His starting salary was $4050, about three times the national average at that time.[131]

After working with a variety of metal alloys, the SL-15 project was Charlie's first chance to work with old-school wooden airplane design. Like the SL-12, the framework and box spars were made from spruce, and the skin was marine-grade mahogany plywood, varnished with Bakelite lacquer.[132] Larsen hoped to fix the vibration problem by adding a fluid coupling between the engine and the drive train, to smooth out the torque pulses from the engine.

The biggest investor in the company was Gilbert Colgate Jr., the great-grandson of the founder of Colgate Palmolive Company. He put $150,000 into the new SL-15 project. Colgate was a dynamic individual, an Olympic medal winner, a co-founder of Planned Parenthood, and a director of Colgate Palmolive. As Charlie later observed, Colgate undoubtedly knew a lot about toothpaste, but not much about aeronautical engineering. But to everyone's annoyance, he began sticking his nose into the aircraft's design and ordering around employees.[133]

In August of 1940, Spencer was fed up with Colgate's interference and resigned. One of their larger investors also backed out. The company was renamed Colgate-Larsen, and the project became the CL-15. Colgate became the chairman of the company, but the wooden seaplane was never built. A year after Spencer left, the company dropped the seaplane project. Larsen soon left as well. The resulting Colgate Aircraft Corporation continued to make airplane parts and did a thriving business during the war.

Charlie was unhappy with the same management situation that had caused Spencer to leave. A few months later, in December, he accepted a job offer from Vultee Aircraft Corporation, in Downey, California (a suburb of Los Angeles); and in January of 1941 he turned in his resignation at Colgate Larsen.

---

[130] Murray, Robert, "The Passion of P.H. Spencer, *Flying Magazine*, October, 1973.; Sloop, John L., *Interview of Mr. K.J. Bossart*, NASA, April 27, 1974.; Larsen, Victor A., *Airplane Drive*, U.S. Patent No. 2,359,652, filed May 13, 1941, issued Oct 3, 1944.

[131] 1940 census data.

[132] *Jane's All the World's Aircraft*, 1948.

[133] Sloop, John L., *Interview of Mr. K.J. Bossart*, NASA, April 27, 1974.; "Historical Resume of Spencer-Larson Aircraft Corporation," National Air and Space Museum, September 19, 1963.

Charlie oversees testing of Sikorsky S-40
(*Courtesy of Vroom Family*).
Illustration of General Aviation GA-38
(*Courtesy of General Motors Archive*).

Inter-Island Airway fleet of S-43s
(*Courtesy of Hawaii State Archive*).

Charlie standing on the chimney of the
Kalmthout home in 1934 (*Courtesy of
Scott Family*).

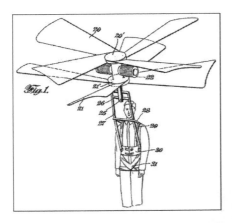

Patent diagrams for De Bothezat's one-man helicopter, a detail of stainless steel wing for E.G. Budd, and Spencer-Larsen sea plane.

Charlie at work at E.G. Budd (*Courtesy of Vroom Family*). Charlie's certificate of citizenship. Charlie and Connie on their wedding day (*Courtesy of Scott Family*).

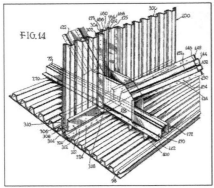

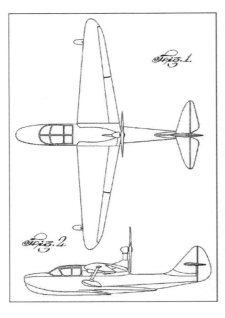

3
Vultee Field

In Europe, the long-expected war had broken out about the time that Charlie was starting at Spencer-Larson. Germany invaded Poland in the fall of 1939. Again, Belgium attempted to remain neutral, but was invaded by Hitler's army in May of 1940. As in the First World War, the Belgians put their faith in defensive fortifications, including a massive anti-tank canal and a group of new fortresses near the German border. The key was Fort Eben-Emael, which guarded the canal. To prepare for its attack, the Germans built a full scale mock-up of the fort and trained an elite team of glider pilots. They flew in and disabled its guns with shaped charges. Trapped inside the fort with no artillery, the Belgian soldiers had no option but to give up.[134] King Leopold III surrendered less than three weeks after the fighting began, a move that was extremely unpopular with the Belgian people.

It had been obvious that trouble was coming, and before war began Charlie had tried to convince his parents and sister to come and stay with his family in America. But Louis decided to remain in his home. Remembering the run on the banks during the First World War, he withdrew all of his savings as gold coins and plastered them into the basement wall of the Kalmthout house. He also mailed some cash to Charlie, for safe keeping. Before the fighting began, Charlie and Connie sent his parents three barrels of supplies, containing flour, sugar and lard. The barrels were almost confiscated by Belgian customs, but Louis finally got to keep them. They were a great help during the harsh rationing and shortages of the long German occupation.

---

[134] Rolf, Rudi and Peter Saal, *Fortress Europe*, Airlife Publishing, 1988.

In the mid-1930s, Charlie's sister was completing her master's degree in physics at the University of Ghent. She spent several months in The Netherlands, using special laboratory facilities at the University of Groningen and worked as a lab assistant with the Nobel Laureate Prof. Frits Zernike.[135] Her thesis on spectroscopy won the Mac Leod Prize for best Dutch physics publication in 1937. While in Gronigen, she met and fell in love with a medical student from South Africa, Frederick "Frik" Scott. They were both fed up with European militarism, and they decided to marry and move to South Africa. With one of his children already overseas, Louis was not happy with that plan, but before they could carry it out, Frik and Dora were trapped in The Netherlands and Belgium for the duration of the war.[136] For a time, before America entered the war, Charlie was able to receive letters from The Netherlands and relay them to Frik's family. The Germans would not permit letters directly to his home because South Africa was part of the British Commonwealth (a fact about which many Afrikaans-speaking citizens were not enthusiastic).[137]

Back in America, Connie was pregnant with their second child when they made the long train trip across the country to Charlie's new job. Jan's new brother, Newell Chase Bossart, was born a few months later. Their first home in California was a rented house in Long Beach.

Charlie started work as the chief of structures in February, 1941. Vultee Aircraft Corporation had been in operation since 1932. The venture was started by the luxury automobile maker E.L. Cord and aircraft designer Gerard Vultee, who had distinguished himself as chief engineer at Lockheed in the late 1920s. At his new company, he developed the eight-passenger V-1 airplane, capable of 235 mph, which was a very impressive speed at that time. Piloting a V-1, the famous aviator Jimmy Doolittle (who had a doctorate degree in aeronautics from MIT) made a record-breaking crossing of the U.S.A., coast to coast in twelve hours.[138]

In 1937, Cord sold his aviation holdings (Vultee, Stinson, and Lycoming Engines) to the New York financier Victor Emanuel. The next year, Vultee and his wife died tragically in the crash of their private plane, but under Emanuel's management, the company survived and prospered.

[135] Bossart, D., *Over relatieve lijnintensiteiten in het emissie-spectrum van molybdeen*, 1936. (On relative line intensities in the emission spectrum of molybdenum).; Le Roux, Ester, "Dora Scott: An Extraordinary Woman", *Culna*, Vol 69, 2014.

[136] Letter to Dora from Frederick Scott, June 1940.

[137] Prof. Retief, "In Memoriam Frederick Petrus Scott," *SA Medical Journal*, February 14, 1976.

[138] Jimmy Doolittle graduated from MIT's aeronautics department months before Charlie Bossart attended. Their careers crossed paths several times and they were good friends.

In spite of the Neutrality Act, which forbade America from entering the war in Europe, President Roosevelt was aggressively preparing for the inevitable. In 1940 he asked Vultee to produce 37,000 aircraft.[139] They tripled the size of their factory and installed the first powered aircraft assembly line in the aviation industry, an innovation no doubt inspired by their long association with automobile manufacturing. Selling trainers and A-31 Vengeance diver bombers, by 1941, Vultee was manufacturing 15 percent of the military aircraft in the U.S.A.[140]

Charlie's new boss was Charles Russell ("Jack") Irvine, the chief development engineer at Vultee. Charlie knew him from their time working at Sikorsky in 1930. After Sikorsky, Irvine had moved to Detroit to join Stinson Aircraft Company. He was one of the designers of the Stinson Reliant, a popular four-passenger private plane. In 1939, Victor Emanuel reorganized his holdings and made Stinson into a division of Vultee. Shortly after the reorganization, Irvine left Detroit and joined the facility at Downey. There, he was tasked with responding to a series of government requests for experimental aircraft. Charlie's old friend Bill Dieter had joined Irvine's team in 1940, and with the intellectual appeal of working on experimental aircraft, it was not surprising that Charlie chose to join them.

During the period between the world wars, the U.S. had hesitated to spend much money on the military. The prevailing view was that the vast oceans surrounding the American continent were the primary defense against enemies in Europe and Asia. But the prospect of entering a war in Europe and engaging their air forces required a change in strategy.

To leap-frog European airplane technology, the U.S. Army Air Corps initiated a number of contracts for experimental aircraft during the pre-war military build-up. In addition, a "hyper engine" research program resulted in new piston motors with high power-to-weight ratios. To stimulate research of more advanced aircraft designs, the Air Corps issued a request for proposals R-40C. It gave two years for testing and prototype development of a fighter-plane capable of 425 to 525 mph at 15,000 feet. This was almost twice the speed of the Air Corps' lackluster fighters and even faster than the latest German Messerschmitt and British Spitfire.[141]

Charlie's first project was the XP-54 experimental pursuit plane, which was already underway when he arrived. The Air Corps request R-40C came out in the fall of 1939, and out of dozens of responses, Vultee's was one of four

[139] Wegg, John, *General Dynamics Aircraft and their Predecessors*, Conway Maritime, 1990.
[140] *The Vultee Aircraft Corporation*, Western Museum of Flight, www.wmof.com.
[141] Boyne, Walter, *Air Warfare*, ABC-Clio, 2002.

chosen to proceed (along with similar projects at Bell, Curtiss and Northrop). In the standard "Fly before you buy" procurement scheme, a non-flying mockup would be built and inspected, then an experimental X-model of a plane would be test flown and modified after the Air Corps gave their feedback. If approved, a Y-model would be built, a prototype of the production aircraft. If the Air Corps was satisfied, it would go into mass production. In June of 1940, Vultee received a small grant for design studies and wind tunnel testing of miniature models. In August and September, they were awarded a total of $1.2 million in contracts to build two XP-54 prototypes.

The XP-54, nicknamed the "Swoose Goose," had a 54-foot wingspan. R-40C specified a rear-propeller "pusher" style of propulsion, and Vultee's design used a single enormous 12 foot propeller. Putting the propeller in the back improved aerodynamics by preventing the fuselage or wings from flying through the wash of its spiral slipstream. The engine was a 2300 horsepower, supercharged, 24-cylinder Lycoming XH-2470 (one of the experimental "hyper engines").

Charlie and his structural analysts had their work cut out for them with such an unusual configuration. One problem with a rear propeller is where to put the rudder and elevators, which normally go on the tail. In Vultee's design, twin booms extended back from the wings and were bridged by a long tail section behind the propeller. The XP-54 was the first aircraft to have an ejection seat, so if a pilot had to bail out, he would not be sucked into the whirling propeller blades behind the cabin.[142]

The XP-54 was primarily made from aluminum, with some steel armor plating in critical areas.[143] For some parts, it also made use of magnesium alloy, lighter than aluminum but not as strong. During wartime, there was a concern about materials availability for production. The problem with aluminum was the massive quantities of electricity needed to extract the metal from its oxide (making a pound of aluminum used enough electricity to supply several homes for a year in those days). That concern was about to be fixed by the new Grand Coulee Dam in Washington State. Its electricity would generate a third of the aluminum used in WWII, much of it for airplanes. Magnesium is the second most common metal in sea water, so it was available in limitless quantities.

Magnesium's lack of stiffness (low Young's modulus) was a challenge for design and stress analysis, but it was still much less elastic than wood. TIG welding was used for construction, an electric arc process that floods

---

[142] Jenkins & Landis, *Experimental & Prototype U.S. Air Force Jet Fighters*, 2008.
[143] Balzer, Gerald H., *American Secret Pusher Fighters of World War II*, 2008.

the work area with helium to avoid oxidation or worse. Every metal had its quirks, and magnesium had a bad one: if it was ignited during welding, the fire would burn in air, water or carbon dioxide, and so was almost impossible to extinguish.

After two years of development, the XP-54 was test flown by Irvine's assistant design engineer Frank Davis. Its maximum speed of 381 mph did not meet the specifications of the request, and it suffered problems with the experimental engine. The plane never advanced beyond the X-model stage, but Vultee gained valuable experience with several new technologies. Eventually, the prototype was turned over to the stress analysis team again. To gather data on structural failure, it was tested to destruction.

By the end of 1941, fighting in Europe had been under way for more than two years, but The Neutrality Act required America to stay out of the conflict. In December, Japan attacked Pearl Harbor and Hitler declared war against the United States. Ultimately, drawing America into the war was a blunder for Germany and Japan. It ensured the defeat of both those countries, not just because America could supply fresh troops, but because its massive economy flooded the war with vehicles, supplies and weapons. The USSR had joined the allies when it was attacked by Germany in April of that year.

The urgency of war and the increased sophistication of aircraft were transforming how the aviation industry designed products, replacing small projects headed by one or two visionaries with complex weapons systems managed and built by large formal organization. Charlie was starting to manage a group of engineers, some of whom would later be part of his Atlas missile team.

Charlie's second project was the experimental one-man attack plane XA-41. Contracted by the Army Air Forces in September, 1942, it was one of the last propeller driven dive-bombers to be built, and only one prototype was completed. When flown in February of 1944, it performed well, but by that time the strategic needs of the Air Forces had changed, and the plane was no longer required.[144] By some accounts, the XA-41 project was continued primarily as an opportunity for Vultee and the Air Forces to study the massive new 28-cylinder 3000-horsepower engine by Pratt & Whitney. Six of these engines were later used on Convair's B-36 bomber.[145]

---

[144] The U.S. Army Air Corps was renamed U.S. Army Air Forces in 1941 and became an independent branch of service, the U.S. Air Force, in 1947.

[145] Van Tuyl and Groenendijk, *A Van Tuyl Chronicle*, 1996.; Darling, Kev, *American X & Y Planes*, Crowood, 2009.

The XA-41 was the last project that Irvine's team worked on under the name of Vultee Aircraft Corporation. In 1941, Vultee's owner, Victor Emanuel, bought control of Consolidated Aircraft Corporation. For a while, he operated Vultee and Consolidated as separate companies, but in March of 1943, he merged them to form the Consolidated Vultee Aircraft Corporation, commonly known as "Convair." Consolidated was even bigger than Vultee. With 45,000 wartime workers, it was the largest private-sector employer in America.[146] During the war, their factory in San Diego built 18,000 B-24 Liberators, comparable to the total bomber production of Nazi Germany.

For the time being, the corporate merger did not drastically change things for the Vultee team or for Charlie. After two years living in Long Beach, he and his family moved to a rental house on Beverly Drive in the suburb of Whittier. It was a large Spanish-style home they nicknamed the "Hacienda," where they raised chickens and had avocado and lemon trees on the property. Whittier was named after a wealthy oil tycoon, whose company developed many of the urban petroleum fields of Los Angeles. Right next door to the Bossart home, a pumpjack see-sawed above an operating oil well.

In the summer of 1943, the Bossart family got a happy addition, with the birth of their daughter Marion. Connie's parents had been sad when Charlie's work took him out to the "wild west," so Newell and Nina Chase came out to stay with their daughter during the birth. One afternoon while the family was relaxing outdoors, the Bossart's rooster began pecking one of the boys and chasing him around the yard. Not approving of this treatment of his grandson, Papa Chase caught the bird and snapped its neck, announcing that it would be their dinner that evening.

A year later, when the owner of the "Hacienda" returned to town, the Bossarts moved again. With the influx of defense-industry workers and high demand for housing, they were lucky to find a rental home not too far from Vultee, on Devlin Street in Norwalk. Their landlord was even kind enough to help them move. Charlie built a white picket fence around the back yard so the children could play outdoors without constant supervision, and they started a vegetable garden (many food supplies were rationed or impossible to obtain during the war). Although there were many wartime hardships, Charlie was living the American dream. To complete the picture, they had a family dog, a wirehaired terrier named "Spot."[147]

---

[146] Pescador, Katrina and Mark Aldrich, *Consolidated Aircraft Corporation*, San Diego Air and Space Museum, 2008.

[147] Post-war letters to his parents detailed Charlie and Connie's life during this time.

At work, in the newly named Vultee Field division of Convair, Irvine's team continued to focus on experimental aircraft. In the summer of 1943, the Army Air Forces issued a seemingly impossible request for a long-range fighter, capable of 1250 mile range, flying at 37,000 feet, and a maximum speed of 500 mph. The objective of the aircraft was to provide escorts for Boeing B-29 Superfortress bombers. At that time, military leaders thought they would be making long-distance attacks from Hawaii against the Japanese mainland, so they needed a fleet of fighters to go along for protection. That September, Convair was the only company to return with a proposal capable of meeting the Air Forces' specifications. Design work began in January.

The project was Charlie's first encounter with jet engines. From the 1920s to the 1940s, work on theory and experiments in jet propulsion were widespread in Europe, America and Russia.[148] The Italian aeronautical engineer, Arturo Crocco, wrote an influential paper on the possibilities of "super aviation," which is what he called high-altitude supersonic flight.[149] In the Soviet Union, Marshal Tukhachevsky described the military value of supersonic aircraft.[150] But it was not until 1930 that the first working turbojet engine was developed and patented, by Frank Whittle of the British Royal Air Force. In April of 1941, the head of the U.S. Army Air Forces, General H.H. "Hap" Arnold, visited England and saw a demonstration of Whittle's engine. A champion of technology and innovation, Arnold arranged for General Electric to license the engine, resulting in the 1600-pound-thrust J-31.

The first concept Irvine considered was a turboprop aircraft augmented with rocket engines, but their analysis of that scheme was not favorable. Instead, the XP-81 was designed with a turbine-driven propeller (turboprop) in the front, and a turbojet engine in the rear (GE's improved 4000-pound-thrust J-33).[151] The turbine-powered propeller was highly efficient and gave the aircraft a long range, while the fuel-guzzling turbojet provided up to 20 minutes of high-speed combat flight, if necessary. This was Convair's first jet aircraft, and the first American aircraft with a turboprop. The modern turbofan engine would later combine both functions in one engine, but at the time, two separate propulsion systems were the only option to meet the objectives of the Air Forces' request.

[148] Smith, G. Geoffrey, "Possibilities of Jet Propulsion," *Flight*, August 28-October 9, 1941.
[149] Crocco, G. Arturo, Possibilita di superaviazione," *Notiziario tecnico di aeronautica*, 1926.
[150] Tukhachevsky, M.N., *Novye Voprosy Voiny (New Problems of War)*, 1932.
[151] Jenkins & Landis, *Experimental & Prototype U.S. Air Force Jet Fighters*, 2008.

The structural design of the plane was semi-monocoque, where the riveted duralumin skin provided much of the strength, but some shape-retaining rings were included inside the hull. Convair received $4.6 million to build two XP-81 prototypes, and one of the planes was test flown in February 1945. Ironically, the biggest problems were not with the jet engine, but with the turboprop and propeller in the front. The engine arrived late, so a piston engine had to be substituted. When the turboprop engine finally arrived in December, it proved to be underpowered and caused problems with vibration. By then the war was over, but the Army Air Forces had lost interest in the plane even before then. The conquest of military bases on islands closer to Japan, such as Guam and Saipan, meant the Air Forces no longer needed long-range missions to bomb the mainland, and the planned production of 13 YP-81s was cancelled.

Before the war's end, Charlie got his first experience with rockets.[152] The Navy was worried about radio-controlled air-to-ship glide bombs such as the American Azon and Bat, and the German Fritz-X. But near the end of 1944, an even more urgent threat appeared. Japan began the desperate and unnerving tactic of flying suicide planes into American ships. Thousands of explosive-filled Kamikazes acted as human-guided cruise missiles. By the end of the war, they had sunk dozens of ships and killed thousands of sailors. The only available countermeasures were fighter planes, anti-aircraft cannons and the newly invented radio proximity fuze (a shell that would explode when it sensed an aircraft's metal body). As a better defense against the Kamikazes, the Navy requested proposals for ship-to-air guided missiles.

Within the Navy's bureaucracy, two branches started ship-to-air-missile projects, and Charlie was involved with both. The Naval Bureau of Aeronautics was in charge of all Naval aircraft, and they considered rockets to be a pilotless aircraft and thus within their purview. They initiated the Lark missile program in late 1944. The Bureau of Ordnance considered rockets to be a form of shipboard artillery, and therefore ship-to-air missiles were their business. They initiated Operation Bumblebee.

The specifications for Lark were worked out by January 1945. The prime contractor was Fairchild, but the Navy asked Convair to develop a back-up, after Fairchild fell behind schedule. Convair's missile carried a 100 pound warhead with a proximity fuze. It was guided by a human operator to its target by aiming a radio beam, which the missile followed ("beam riding"). The 18-foot missile would fly at 650 mph, faster than any plane

152 Chapman, John L., *Atlas: The Story of a Missile*, Harper, New York, 1960.

could evade. It was powered by a liquid-fuel rocket engine manufactured by Reaction Motors Inc, in New Jersey. Charlie's structural analysis had to deal with acceleration and speed far beyond what aircraft experienced. Most of the missile hull was made from aluminum, but steel was used in the central section where the stabilization fins were subject to the highest aerodynamic stresses.

The Navy hoped that a crash program could develop the missile in six months, but the war ended well before it was completed. A successful test was made in December, 1947, and it became the first U.S. missile to shoot down a moving test aircraft.[153] Work continued until 1950, when it was cancelled in favor of the rival Bumblebee project.[154]

The initial plan for Bumblebee, in December of 1944, was a supersonic ramjet-powered missile named Talos. Convair did not get the contract, but they were hired to work on a supersonic test vehicle (STV) powered by a solid-fuel rocket. Its purpose was to test the guidance system. Ultimately, the STV proved to be more successful than the complicated Talos. It was chosen for further development and became the Terrier missile.[155]

Although the STV was a solid-fuel rocket, Vultee Field was also involved in researching ramjet engines for the Bumblebee project. The ramjet was a simple form of the jet engine, with no turbine or compressor blades. It was a simple tube with a constriction in the middle. At very high speed, air was forced into it by the forward motion of the aircraft, compressed at the constriction where combustion would take place, and then exhausted through a nozzle at the rear. Before it could start, it had to be accelerated to a high speed, for example by a solid-fuel rocket first stage.

Convair managed the Ordnance Aerophysics Lab in Daingerfield, Texas, where the world's largest supersonic wind tunnels went into operation in the fall of 1945. In October, they began building experimental ramjet engines for testing at that facility.[156] This furthered the experience of Irvine's team in the field of rocket and jet propulsion.

When the Lark and Bumblebee projects began, the war was already nearing its end. In Europe, the tide was clearly turning against Germany by 1944. On September 4, British forces retook Charlie's home city of Antwerp. Even though the Allies were pushing the Germans back on the Eastern and

[153] "Missile, Surface-to-Air, Lark," Collections, Smithsonian National Air and Space Museum.; "New Weapon Disclosed," *New York Times*, August 15, 1949.
[154] McMurran, William, *Achieving Accuracy: A Legacy of Computers and Missiles*, 2008.
[155] Wilson, Gill Robb, "Convair: Industrial Giant of the Air Age," *Flying Magazine*, Jul-Oct, 1960.
[156] Welty, Howard, Notes on C.R. Irvine Weekly Engineering Working Reports, San Diego Aerospace Museum.

Western fronts, the liberation of Antwerp at such an early stage was a bold move. The German occupation forces had rigged bridges and port facilities for demolition, but a brave Belgian engineer named Robert Vekemans had noted where they were placing explosives. He contacted the advancing British forces and convinced the commander to make a sudden push to Antwerp and surprise the Germans. The German occupying force surrendered after brief fighting, before they could carry out the planned destruction of the port.

Antwerp was a prize of incredible strategic value: 30 miles of docks, more than 600 loading cranes, 900 warehouses and a vast rail network. After the Scheldt river was swept for mines, the port was ready for use. It could handle a thousand ships per month, and half of Allied supplies were soon flowing into Europe via the port. The massive influx of Allied shipping was an economic boon to the city and would help it recover from war-time damage. But this activity also made Antwerp one of Germany's highest-priority targets. In December, they staged a major offensive, attempting to recapture Antwerp. It became known as the Battle of the Bulge.

Himmler ordered Germany's "vengeance weapons," the V-1 and V-2 missiles, to focus on Antwerp's port, in hopes of demolishing it from afar. These were unique new weapons, capable of delivering a ton of explosive to a distance of two hundred miles.

The V-1 was a cruise missile, a winged unmanned aircraft controlled by a simple gyroscopic autopilot. It was propelled by a loud pulse-jet engine that signaled its approach and earned it the nickname of "buzz bomb". Cruising at 350 mph, they were fast by the standards of those times, but not too fast to shoot down.

The V-2 was a ballistic missile, a rocket that took off vertically, flew high into the ionosphere and fell on its target without warning at more than twice the speed of sound. The term "ballistic" refers to an object flying through the air freely, without propulsion, such as a bullet or artillery shell (the word is derived from the Latin "ballista", an ancient form of catapult). It was applied to missiles like the V-2 because they accelerated by rocket engine for a short time and then spent most of the flight as a ballistic projectile.

The V-2 captured the popular imagination. It was an order of magnitude larger than any rocket built before. The first of these missiles were launched in combat on September 8, 1944, against Paris, but London became the first major target. The bombardment of London is famous, with 1358 rockets launched at the city. But an even larger number of rockets were aimed at Antwerp: 1610 in all.

Both types of V-weapons were quite inaccurate, so their impacts were scattered throughout the city and its suburbs. Up until then, Antwerp had been almost untouched by the war. But starting in October, months of missile bombardment damaged or destroyed half the buildings in the city. The most tragic incident was the strike on the Rex Cinema, where a V-2 killed 567 movie viewers.[157] It was the deadliest V-2 strike anywhere during the war.

Despite all attempts by Germany to disrupt the port of Antwerp, it continued to operate and supply the Allies. By February of 1945, Western and Soviet forces had pushed into Germany, and the war was all but lost for Hitler. He committed suicide on April 30, and Germany surrendered a week later. Japan was pushed back across the Pacific but continued fighting until America dropped atomic bombs in August. Japan surrendered a week later.

During the war, Charlie had had no contact with his parents and sister, and he was deeply worried about them. He and his wife were excited and relieved when they got their first letter from Louis, in February of 1945.[158] In the liberation of Antwerp, one brief battle came near the Bossart home, when French and German forces clashed in northern Kalmthout. Only a couple errant V-2s landed in Kalmthout, which was far to the north of the port. However, the more primitive V-1s were scattered over a wider area, and more than a hundred landed there. Kalmthout was well outside the air-defense zone that protected the harbor, so there was nothing to stop missiles that landed there. One of these "buzz bombs" landed on Duinzicht Lane, only 100 yards from their home, and the concussion broke many of the windows in their house.[159] With no coal rations, the broken windows made the winter of 1944-45 all the more miserable for Charlie's parents.

As soon as it was possible, Charlie and Connie began sending packages to relatives in Belgium, limited for a time by postal regulations on weight and number of mailings. They concentrated on clothing and difficult-to-find foodstuffs such as canned meat, chocolate and coffee. Charlie pelted his father with questions: Was anyone they knew hurt? How were the Van

---

[157] "City of Sudden Death," *TIME*, March 26, 1945.
[158] Letters spanning 1945 to 1950 from Charlie and Connie to his parents were kindly supplied to the author Jan Vroom, the grandson of Aunt Vire Dent.
[159] Letters from Louis to Dora, 1946; A map entitled: *Antwerp V1 and V2 attack: fall of shot on arrondissement of Antwerp from 7 Oct. 44 to 30 March 45.*

Overloops and Aunt Vire? Was the landmark tower of Our Lady Cathedral still standing?

He learned that the Germans had taken over and occupied Aunt Vire's hotel, De Kievit. The most tragic news was about Vire's son, Russell Jr., who had died of a brain hemorrhage. He had been working as a shop boy in Coventry, England, and may have suffered a head injury in the infamous German bombing raid a few weeks before his death.[160] Vire's remaining child was her daughter, Elvire "Daisy" Dent.

Some good news was that Dora and Frik had gotten married. She had not been permitted to travel from Belgium to The Netherlands until the Germans issued a permit in 1943, and the couple was wed that September. They moved to Leeuwarden, where they stayed at a friend's house. A year later, they had their first son, Willem.

At the start of the German occupation, Frik had been briefly interned in a camp for foreign citizens, but he was soon released and permitted to practice medicine. German officials gave him special permission to ride a bicycle when visiting patients, but with a warning that any German (civilian or military) had a right to confiscate it for their own use. Near the end of the war, Germans were rounding up able-bodied men to work in Nazi factories. Frik was officially excepted from forced labor, but the couple kept a low profile to minimize the chance of being snatched off the streets.[161]

When the war was over, Dora and Frik took a ferry to Britain, and after three months in the Bridge of Weir transit camp, they got a ship to South Africa. It was a non-stop voyage of 18 days, and Dora arrived at her new home in December 1945. Frik began a medical practice in Edenville in the Orange Free State. It was a rustic town, and their first home did not have running water; but it was a wonderful life compared to Nazi-occupied Netherlands.

The Bossarts wanted to visit Dora, and Charlie turned this dream into a series of stories for his children, to teach them about science and geography. In an imaginary journey to Dora and Frik's home, they would ride a blimp across America and over the Atlantic Ocean to Africa. He told them about the animals that lived there, including the ostrich, a flightless bird so big that the boys could ride on one, and then eat the giant eggs for breakfast. When Dora informed Charlie that they had no ostriches in South Africa, he joked to her, "Couldn't you get just one for when we come and visit you? If the Bossart family gets there and there is no ostrich—why our

---

[160] Russell Jr. died on December 18, 1940. The death certificate lists "cerebral aneurysm" as cause of death. His sister Daisy later wrote that he died in the bombing.

[161] Various official documents of the occupation government, saved by Dora.

boys just won't give a plugged nickel for Daddy's knowledge of natural history."[162]

As the post-war era began, the Army Air Forces turned its attention to new weapons requirements. Several new developments informed planning for aircraft: the jet engine, discoveries in high-velocity aerodynamics, and the strategic consequences of atomic weapons. In August of 1945, several requests for designs were issued to the aviation industry. These would be the last experimental aircraft projects that Charlie and Jack Irvine worked on, and like the Navy missile projects, they required the analysis of stresses at supersonic and near-supersonic speed.

One of the requests was for a "penetration fighter," an aircraft meant for long-range fighter missions. Convair's proposal, internally named model VF-4511, was powered by three Westinghouse turbojet engines. It had an estimated top speed of 657 mph and a combat radius of 900 miles. But even though the Air Forces gave the design the highest marks, they cancelled the project before it reached the X-model prototype phase. Some in Washington felt too many contracts were being awarded to Convair.[163]

The penetration fighter contained an important new aerodynamics innovation: the back-swept wing. Up until then, airplane wings extended perpendicular from the fuselage, but some aerodynamics theorists proposed that a swept back wing could avoid dangerous instability that occurred close to the speed of sound. The swept-wing concept had been floating around the aviation industry for several years, but it was viewed with skepticism until events in Europe led to sudden enthusiasm for the idea.

On April 12, American forces captured a site in Völkenrode that at first appeared to be a farm. But the cleverly camouflaged installation was actually a secret aviation research laboratory, headed by Adolph Busemann, one of Germany's leading aerodynamicists.[164] The Americans quickly brought in a team of scientists who had been touring German aeronautics facilities in occupied territory. Among the site's dozens of facilities was the largest supersonic wind tunnel in Germany, and the science team found aircraft models and test data that demonstrated the advantages of the swept-back wing at very high velocities.

The leader of the Army Air Forces science team was the renowned professor of aerodynamics, Theodore von Kármán.[165] He was the founder

[162] Letter to Louis, August 27 1945; Letter to Dora, May 6, 1946. (There is actually a southern variety of ostrich, so Charlie was not completely mistaken).
[163] Bradley, Robert E., *Convair Advanced Designs II*, Crecy, 2013
[164] The Herman Göring Aeronautical Research Center.
[165] Tódor von Skolloskislaki Kármán (1881-1963).

of Caltech's Jet Propulsion Laboratory and General Hap Arnold's chief technical advisor. Von Kármán had been present in 1935 when Busemann presented his swept-wing theory at an international conference, but his work went largely unnoticed.[166]

Outside of Germany, not everyone ignored Busemann's idea. In 1941, Sikorsky's chief engineer, Michael Gluhareff, proposed a dart-shaped plane with a swept delta wing. At Langley Laboratory, Robert T. Jones studied Gluhareff's design and independently formulated a theory for swept wings and delta wings. However, experts in the American aeronautics community were skeptical even after Jones performed some high-speed tests on models. The Army's supersonic wind tunnel at Aberdeen, Maryland became operational in 1944, and Jones' ideas were further tested there by von Kármán. So he and others in the science team were keenly aware of the importance of the German experiments, which were viewed as a confirmation of the swept-wing concept.[167]

Another project that Charlie worked on at Vultee Field would push beyond the swept-wing concept and produce a historic airplane: the world's first delta-wing jet. The delta-wing was a triangular wing (shaped like the Greek letter delta: Δ). On the leading edge, the wing was swept back, but the rear edge was perpendicular to the body of the airplane.

The Army Air Forces request was for a point-defense fighter, to defend cities and critical military bases against bombers. With the advent of the atomic bomb, air defense had become an urgent necessity. With anti-aircraft missiles still in early stages of development, only a fast fighter plane could take off and shoot down an incoming bomber before it caused incredible destruction. The Air Forces' specifications were extraordinary: a maximum speed of 700 mph, and the ability to climb to 50,000 feet in four minutes. Based on the Völkenrode supersonic wind tunnel tests and on the theoretical work by Robert T. Jones, Convair's engineers expected swept-wing design would be necessary to meet those requirements.

In addition to the swept-wing idea, they chose to use rockets to augment the thrust of a jet engine. In those days, the term jet propulsion meant rockets as well as jet engines. In America, before and during the war, there had been extensive research on rockets and ramjets, but not much on turbojets, until they were licensed from Britain.

---

[166] Samuel, Wolfgang, *American Raiders: The Race to Capture the Luftwaffe's Secrets*, University of Mississippi Press, 2004.
[167] Von Kármán, Theodore, *Aerodynamics: Selected topics in the light of their historical developments*, Cornell, 1957.; Von Kármán, Theodore, *Where We Stand: A Report Prepared for the AAF Scientific Advisory Group*, August, 1945.

On October 13, Convair presented their interceptor design to Air Materials Command at Wright Patterson AFB. They proposed wings with a median sweep of 35°, and a 35-foot 4-inch span. For propulsion, it would contain a Westinghouse turbojet engine. For rapid ascent and combat it would also have six 1500-pound-thrust rocket engines in the tail. The rockets would give it an enormous speed boost, but they consumed fuel at a furious rate, using it up in just a few minutes. Their fuel was nitro-methane and concentrated hydrogen peroxide, dangerously unstable propellants.

In April 1946, Convair won the contest for the point-defense interceptor, now designated XP-92. They began making small-scale models to distribute to the Air Forces and a full-size skeleton version for stress analysis. Soon, they received a contract of $5.3 million to develop a full-scale mock-up for inspection, followed by two X-model flying prototypes.

In mid-May, Ralph Shick, Irvine's Chief of Aerodynamics, suggested they use some of the scale models for testing in Vultee's subsonic wind tunnel, and subsequently in the supersonic tunnel at Caltech. He immediately found a problem with "wing-tip stall." As other designers soon found, a swept wing generated a vortex, reducing lift at the tips and creating a backwash that pushed down the tail of the plane. This caused the nose to pitch up, which could cause a stall, loss of control or even stress the wings to the breaking point. To reduce the stalling effect, Shick increased the sweep angle to 45° and then 60°. In the first week of July, he decided to increase the wing's lift by "filling in" the wing to form a triangular delta airfoil.

Shick had arrived at a delta wing, which had been explored by the Germans and by Jones at Langley Labs; but Shick had reached that design in small steps, after 5000 hours of wind-tunnel experiments and reshaping of wing.[168] During a trip to Wright Patterson AFB, he talked to several German aerodynamicists, including Alexander Lippisch, who was a major proponent of the delta wing. Lippisch had proposed a thick delta wing, but Convair used a thin wing, which Jones demonstrated was more advantageous at near-supersonic speeds. In addition to Lippisch's technical advice, Shick wanted the Germans to endorse Convair's delta wing and bolster the Air Forces' confidence in the design.[169]

---

[168] Bradley, Robert E., *Convair Advanced Designs II*, Crecy, 2013.; Hallion, Richard, "Convair's Delta Alpha," *Air Enthusiast Quarterly*, June, 1976.

[169] Welty, Howard, Notes on C.R. Irvine's working reports. Lippisch had built a full-size wooden model of a thick-winged delta plane, which NACA put in their wind tunnel. Its structure was only able to withstand testing up to 45 mph, so little was learned about its behavior at supersonic speed. It is still a popular myth that the Convair design was simply copied from Lippisch's wooden model (e.g., Wikipedia article on Convair XF-92).

In September, Convair proposed, and the Army Air Forces agreed, that so many innovations were contained in the interceptor design that it should be divided into two projects. XP-92 would focus on experimental jet propulsion systems, exploring a novel scheme that was a hybrid between a rocket and a ramjet engine. Convair hoped their engine could propel the jet at twice the speed of sound. By 1946, Charlie was involved with rocket projects, but he still worked on the stress analysis of XP-92.[170] To study the delta wing concept, XF-92A would be a flying aircraft with a conventional jet engine. The propulsion experiments were eventually canceled, but the XF-92A was built and flown in September 1948. This was the world's first delta-wing jet aircraft. Although its engine was not powerful enough to reach supersonic speed in level flight, the plane broke the sound barrier during dive tests (the straight-winged Bell X-1 had been first to fly supersonic in October of 1947).

The experimental XF-92A was followed by the F-102 Delta Dagger, which was able to fly at Mach 1.25 (1.25 times the speed of sound). Convair sold more than a thousand of them to the Air Force. It was followed by the F-106, which could cruise at Mach 2. These planes were used for a variety of missions, but most importantly, they were deployed to intercept incoming Soviet bombers that might carry nuclear weapons.

In the course of this work at Convair, Charlie also made contributions to the techniques of stress analysis. In the late 1930s, the field had been revolutionized by the invention of the strain gauge. These zigzag-shaped foil sensors were cemented to a surface and allowed engineers to measure microscopic stretching and compression of the structure. This meant that strain could be directly measured rather than just calculated. Measurements from clusters of strain gauges in different orientations, called "rosettes," could be combined mathematically to measure complex forms of strain such as shearing, twisting, and bending. Charlie quickly mastered and improved on the complex mathematics of that technique.[171] He worked with a young consulting engineer named Given Brewer, who had worked on the stress analysis of Consolidated's B-24 bomber. Brewer went on to become a leading figure in the field of experimental stress analysis.

---

[170] Bossart, K.J., "Design Problems of Large Rockets," *High Altitude and Satellite Rockets, Cranfield Symposium*, July 18-20, 1957. (biography on page 132).

[171] Bossart, K.J., G.A. Brewer, "A Graphical Method of Rosette Analysis," *Proceedings of the Society for Experimental Stress Analysis*, 4(1), 1946.

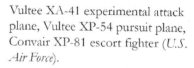

Vultee XA-41 experimental attack
plane, Vultee XP-54 pursuit plane,
Convair XP-81 escort fighter (*U.S.
Air Force*).

Convair XP-92A delta wing fighter
(*NASA Dryden Research*). Convair
Lark missile in NACA wind tunnel
(*NASA*).

Family portrait: Jan, Charlie, Marion,
Connie Newell (*Courtesy of Bossart
Family*).

4

MX-774

"The weapons of today are the museum pieces of tomorrow," said General Hap Arnold.[172] Head of the Army Air Forces during the Second World War, Arnold was uniquely qualified to advocate for missile technology. In 1917, Arnold had worked with a group of scientists on the world's first guided missile: the Kettering Aerial Torpedo.[173] This was a cruise missile consisting of an airplane filled with explosive and guided by a Sperry autopilot. In 1941, General Arnold considered using these missiles, but the Allies had no territory from which it could reach the industrial heartland of Germany.

When the problem of nuclear-armed intercontinental missiles was first considered, the major question was which of two types of missiles should it be: a cruise missile like the V-1, or a ballistic missile like the V-2? While the ballistic rocket concept eventually won out, its superiority was not immediately obvious to everyone.

War rockets had a long history and a mixed reputation among military experts. They became prominent at the end of the 18th century, when the Indian leader Tipu Sultan surprised and defeated British forces with rocket-propelled grenades. The innovation was using a strong iron tube, able to contain high exhaust pressure and give the rockets a range of almost a mile. The British were quick to learn a lesson from their defeat, and Sir William Congreve, head of a royal ordnance laboratory, improved on the Indian design. His rockets could be tipped with fragmentation grenades, explosive or incendiary warheads. In 1807, they burned a third of Copenhagen to the

---

[172] Arnold, H.H., "Air Power for Peace," *National Geographic*, February 1, 1946.
[173] Arnold, H.H., *Global Mission*, Harper, 1949.

ground with these war rockets, and the famous line from the American national anthem, "the rocket's red glare" referred to Congreve rockets used against Fort McHenry in the War of 1812.

War rockets were popular for a while, but after a few decades, artillery cannons caught up with and surpassed the range of rockets. More importantly, artillery was accurate. After a shell leaves the gun barrel, its acceleration is finished, and the course is a predetermined ballistic trajectory. However, a rocket accelerates while traveling freely through the air and can wobble and veer off course.

The war rocket came back dramatically in the Second World War, with the advent of the V-2. The project was the vision of one of Germany's foremost experts on ballistics, a military PhD engineer named Karl Becker. This was the same man who helped design the "Big Bertha" howitzer that had pounded the fortifications of Antwerp. After the First World War, Becker concluded that artillery technology had reached its limits.

Those limits were exemplified by the 112-foot cannon used to shell Paris from 75 miles away. The so-called Paris Gun was built by the Krupp munitions firm.[174] Its performance was due in part to sheer power, using 440 pounds of smokeless powder. In part, the range was due to wind-tunnel studies, by Becker and his colleagues, to optimize the supersonic aerodynamics of artillery shells (studies which also determined the shape of the V-2 fuselage). But the Paris Guns had many problems. The barrels were so damaged by breech pressures of over 4000 atmospheres that they only survived 60 to 70 shots. Krupp re-bored them to a slightly larger caliber, so they could be used a second time. During the shelling of Paris, one of the guns exploded, killing its crew. All in all, the guns were impractical.

Becker concluded that rockets were the future of long-range artillery. He believed that the newly invented liquid-fuel engines could provide almost unlimited range. To solve the problem of accuracy, he hoped to use gyroscopic guidance. A rapidly spinning wheel (up to 60,000 rpm) mounted in gimbals remains in a fixed orientation and provides an internal sense of direction for a vehicle. Underwater torpedoes had used gyroscopic guidance since the 1890s, so it was not surprising that many people independently thought of using the technique for rockets.

In 1929, he began a research and development project in the German Army, hiring another military engineer Walter Dornberger to oversee it. They contracted with Heylandt Corporation, which built the first practical German liquid-fuel engines. They began working with Siemens and

---

[174] Bull and Murphy, *Paris Kanonen*, Mittler, Bonn, 1988.

Kreiselgeräte companies on gyroscopic guidance, and they enlisted another company to build a radio-beam guidance system.

They also funded some of the amateur rocket clubs that built crude liquid-fueled rockets. Becker and Dornberger were not impressed by the feuding among rival space clubs and their sensationalist, unscientific methods,[175] but they were much taken by one junior rocket enthusiast: Wernher von Braun. They hired him, and Becker arranged for him to do a Ph.D. thesis on rocket engines. Von Braun won these opportunities in part because his father was a cabinet minister in the conservative Papen administration, but the army engineers genuinely admired his polite aristocratic personality and obvious talent. Von Braun proved to be one of the world's great project managers, with an ability to grasp what everyone was working on and inspire them to do their best.[176]

Becker had hoped that gyroscopic guidance would make the V-2 as accurate as artillery, but the technology of the time was not advanced enough. The missile was originally specified to have an accuracy of 0.5 miles, but in reality it landed randomly within a circle 9 miles in diameter. The missiles also malfunctioned frequently or disintegrated during flight.[177]

In spite of these technical shortcomings, engineers and the general public were fascinated by the V-2. In addition to exploring the enemy's aircraft technology, General Arnold asked von Kármán to investigate the German rocket program. The professor returned to Europe in October of 1945 to witness British test launches of captured V-2s. At the time, no one could have realized what an extraordinary gathering of people came to the British tests. Von Kármán brought his most brilliant graduate student, H.S. Tsien,[178] who would one day found the Chinese space program.

The party of witnesses from the Soviet Union included their top rocket designer, Sergei Korolev,[179] the man who would one day build the Russian ICBM and launch Sputnik. None of the other scientists in attendance would get to know him, however. To keep him incognito during the British V-2 test, he was disguised as a chauffeur.[180]

Charlie's future Soviet counterpart was also a student of aeronautics. At the Kiev Polytechnic Institute, Korolev built gliders for an annual contest in Ukraine. In 1926, he moved to Moscow and studied under Andrei Tupolev,

---

[175] Dornberger, Walter, *V-2 The Nazi Rocket Weapon*, Ballantine, 1954.

[176] Neufeld, Michael, *Von Braun: Dreamer of Space, Engineer of War*, Knopf, New York, 2007.

[177] Kloeppel, Major Kirk M., The Military Utility of German Rocketry During World War II, 1997.

[178] Hsue-Shen Tsien (1911-2009), spelled Qian Xuesen in modern transliteration.

[179] Sergei Pavlovich Korolev (1907-1966).

[180] Chertok, Boris, *Rockets and People: Volume I*, NASA, 2005. (Translation by Asif Siddiqi)

the foremost aircraft designer to remain after the communist revolution. The period from the late 1920s to the early 1930s was an era of exploration. The Soviet Union sent airplanes to the North Pole, probed the stratosphere with giant balloons, and formed the Society for Studies of Interplanetary Travel.[181] Founded in 1924, the Russian space travel society predated the first German rocket club by several years. Korolev became a department head in a jet-propulsion research bureau, working on rocket-powered airplanes. His interest in those days was high-altitude supersonic flight, not space travel and ballistic missiles. However, his group did build and launch a liquid fuel rocket in 1933.

The first phase of Korolev's career was cut short in 1938. The visionary patron of jet propulsion research, Marshall Tukhachevsky, was executed in Stalin's political purges, and soon afterwards the managers of the jet research bureau were also killed. Korolev and other engineers were arrested on false charges of anti-Soviet activity and sabotage. In some cases, the men were beaten until they denounced each other; Korolev's jaw was broken before he signed a confession. Among other charges, he was accused of sabotaging a prototype rocket plane. The allegedly destroyed aircraft was parked conspicuously outside the lab, undamaged for all to see, but Korolev was still found guilty. Sent to a Soviet labor camp in Siberia, he would certainly have perished if it were not for Andrei Tupolev. His old mentor saved Korolev's life by getting him reassigned to work as a prisoner in a war-time aircraft factory.[182]

After the war, Stalin realized the Soviet Union needed a crash program to modernize its military technology. He created three "special committees" to investigate radar, the atomic bomb, and jet propulsion. The jet-propulsion committee's responsibilities included turbojet aircraft, anti-aircraft missiles, and long-range rockets. As Russia's leading expert on rocketry, Korolev was hastily freed from prison and "rehabilitated" to act as chief engineer of the ballistic missile effort.

In America, there was extensive research on rockets during the 1930s and 1940s.[183] Best known was Goddard's pioneering work in New Mexico. His rocket technology was the most advanced in the world until the massively funded V-2 project caught up with him. Goddard worked with the government, but was secretive and uncooperative with other rocket groups in America. At Caltech, von Kármán and his students founded the Jet

---

[181] *Obshchestvo Izucheniya Mezhplanetnykh Soobshcheny*

[182] Siddiqi, Asif, *The Red Rockets' Glare*, Cambridge University Press, 2010. (Tupolev was himself a prisoner in his factory.). Golovanov, *Korolev Fakty I Mify*, Nauka, Moscow, 1994.

[183] Winter, Frank H., *Prelude to the Space Age, The Rocket Societies: 1924-1940*, Smithsonian Inst. 1983.

Propulsion Laboratory in 1936, and in 1942, some of them started the Aerojet Engineering Corporation, to manufacture rocket engines for the Army Air Forces. On the East Coast, the American Rocket Society spawned Reaction Motors Incorporated, which made rockets for the Navy.

Before the war, there were advocates in the United States for building long-range rockets. In 1939, Major James Randolph wrote a famous and provocative article about rockets in the journal of Army Ordnance.[184] He proposed building "ocean-crossing" rockets with a range of 3000 miles. Goddard also presented the idea of large ballistic missiles to the Army. He was annoyed by Randolph's paper, because he believed such work should be discussed in strict secrecy, not in the open literature.[185] The most ambitious effort in America was von Kármán's Corporal missile, in 1944. It was planned to have a range of 60 miles, but it was not completed until years after the war.

The U.S. military did not fund a giant-rocket project, and that was probably a wise decision. In many ways, the V-2 was a strategic blunder. The cost of developing and manufacturing the rocket was comparable to the cost of building the Luftwaffe's fighter aircraft fleet, and one historian concluded that the V-2 wasted so much manpower and resources that it contributed to the Allied victory.[186] During the war, the British did a parametric cost-benefit analysis of the V-2 versus the Heinkel He-111 bomber, and they concluded that Germany should have spent their resources on the bombers. But the German military never carried out its own analysis of how effective the V-2 would be.[187]

When Charlie was later shown diagrams of the V-2 missile, he had the same reaction, that it was a waste of money to build a vehicle as expensive as an airplane that only delivered one bomb.[188] America had invested more wisely in projects of similar cost and complexity but greater strategic value: the atomic bomb, automatic radar tracking, the B-29 Superfortress, and the radio proximity fuze.

After the war, strategic thinking about long-range rockets became more positive. In von Kármán's first report after visiting Germany, he proposed a rocket with a range of 6000 miles, able to reach the Japanese mainland from the U.S. west coast.[189] Most importantly, he pointed out that a long-range rocket could carry an atomic bomb. With a nuclear warhead, a long-range

---

[184] Randolph. James R., "What Can We Expect of Rockets?," *Army Ordnance*, January, 1939.

[185] Goddard, Esther, Pendray G. Edward, *The Papers of Robert H. Goddard*, McGraw Hill, 1970.

[186] Neufeld, Michael J., The Rocket and the Reich, The Free Press, 1995, p 274.

[187] Kloeppel, Major Kirk M., The Military Utility of German Rocketry During World War II, 1997.

[188] Chapman, John L., *Atlas: The Story of a Missile*, Harper, New York, 1960.

[189] Von Kármán, Theodore, *Where We Stand*, August, 1945.

rocket became a whole new kind of weapon. They became more cost effective (more bang for the buck, so to speak), and the A-bomb's wide area of destruction did not require the pin-point accuracy of a conventional bomb.

The Army, Navy and Army Air Forces each began independent rocket research efforts, influenced in varying degrees by the V-2. The Army brought captured German engineers, including Wernher von Braun, to the Redstone Arsenal, in Huntsville Alabama. They began work on a successor to the V-2, known as the Redstone rocket. Captured V-2 missiles were brought to the White Sands proving ground, in New Mexico, and many of them were used for scientific experiments, fired vertically to probe conditions in the ionosphere for a few minutes before falling back to Earth. The Navy funded work on the Viking rocket, designed to replace the dwindling supply of V-2s for vertical upper-atmospheric research.

In the Army Air Forces, General Arnold was interested in a rocket far more powerful than what the Germans were building for the Army. Rather than build an in-house research team, he turned to the aviation industry. On October 31, 1945, the Air Force issued a request for proposals (RFP), just as they would have done for an aircraft. The task was to study surface-to-surface missiles in four range categories: 20-175, 175-500, 500-1500 and 1500-5000 miles.[190] Only the first and shortest category was familiar territory. American glide bombs and short-range missiles reached 20 miles; and 175 miles was the nominal range of the V-2, which was the upper limit of rocket power at that time.

Convair Corporation was busy with the B-36 intercontinental bomber; but Irvine's experimental group at Vultee Field had worked on the Lark and Bumblebee missiles, so they were assigned to respond to the missile RFP. They decided to tackle the most challenging category, the 5000-mile range. That missile was specified to carry a 5000-pound atomic warhead, and have an accuracy of 5000 feet. In January of 1946, Convair submitted two concepts. The first was a subsonic turbojet-powered cruise missile. The second was a rocket, only slightly bigger than the V-2, but optimistically specified to fly 25 times as far. In April, the Air Forces awarded Convair a $1.4 million contract to study and compare the two designs. The project was assigned the code name MX-774 (MX for experimental missile).

The only other company to propose a 5000-mile-range missile was Northrop, with a turbojet cruise missile called "Snark" (MX-775). North

[190] Neufeld, Jacob, *The Development of Ballistic Missiles in the United States Air Force, 1945-1960*, Office of Air Force History, Washington, 1990.

American Aviation proposed a 500-mile boost-glide cruise missile, powered by a rocket and ramjet. This became the "Navaho" missile (MX-770), which evolved over time into a 5000-mile-range supersonic cruise missile. But only Convair proposed the option of an intercontinental ballistic rocket.

Unlike many pioneers of rocketry, Charlie was never fascinated by rockets and space travel in his youth.[191] But he loved challenging engineering problems. After working on Convair's initial response to the RFP, his calculations convinced him that a 5000-mile range was possible for a rocket. He let Irvine know that he was interested in leading the effort. Charlie was already Chief of Structures, but now he was seeking a job as a project manager, which technically was a demotion. But corporate rank was never of any importance to him.

Charlie had proven his mastery and creativity in his field, but now he was asking to head a project that could have national importance. Management said yes to his request to run the missile project; but the next day, to Charlie's disappointment, they told him it might be assigned to someone else. Luckily they changed their minds again and gave him command of the MX-774 project.[192]

The fascinating new job came along just as Charlie and Connie were wondering whether to stay in California or move on to a new employer. In 1942, Princeton University had approached Charlie with an offer to start an aeronautics department, but at that time, he felt a duty to stay at Vultee and help with the war effort.[193] Now there was another good reason to stay.

He assembled a project team, including an inner circle of five men. His assistant project engineer was Lloyd William Standley, a mechanical engineer and a ten-year employee of Consolidated Aircraft Co. Specializing in hydraulic and pneumatic control systems, he had worked with Charlie on the Bumblebee missile project. Charles Stuart Ames had been a production chief with Army Ordnance for ten years and recently joined Convair to work on Bumblebee. James Wesley Crooks Jr. was an electrical engineer who had just graduated from Kansas State University. A giant of a man, over six and a half feet tall, he had been a child prodigy in the field of electronics. Cleon Judson Holden was a Naval Academy graduate and an engineer in the weights group. And finally, William Howell Patterson was a physicist who had been a captain in the Army, in charge of a radar-guided anti-aircraft unit during the war. MX-774 was Patterson's first job with Convair, where he did aerodynamics studies.[194]

---

[191] Stone, Frank, "Charlie Bossart: Stroller Gazes at the Sky," *San Diego Evening Tribune*, March 12, 1960.

[192] "Bossart Wins M/R Goddard Trophy," *Missiles and Rockets*, Feb 15, 1960.

[193] Letter to Charlie's parents, August 27, 1945.

Like Sikorsky, Charlie was open-minded but demanded rigorous scientific validation of ideas and designs. He came to work in the morning with notes and calculations written at home the night before. During the day, he would stop by his team members and pose problems for them to work on. At the end of the day, they all gathered around the conference table for a couple hours to discuss their progress and brain storm.[195]

His personality inspired devotion to the project. Richard Martin, one of his structural engineers, said, "I found Charlie Bossart to be one of the kindest, most good-natured persons I have ever known. He let others think that they were discovering things for the first time."[196] Bill Patterson later said, "He had the gift of picking good people and they would work for him until they dropped."[197]

At home, Charlie and Connie were exchanging letters with his parents in Antwerp. Connie had met them before her marriage, in the 1930s, when they visited the Chase family in Baltimore. Now she and Louis were forming a bond over their common interest in education. Charlie and Connie were not happy with the school in Norwalk, and she began to augment Jan's education with lesson plans from Calvert School in Baltimore (producers of a famous homeschooling curriculum). In December, 1945, the boy broke his leg on a small merry-go-round (with some accidental help from his brother Newell), and they kept him out of school for a year. Connie turned to Louis for advice about home schooling, and he sent her work books of his own devising and some textbooks published in London. He also wrote short stories for her to read to the children, much to their delight.

The highest compliment that Connie paid to Louis was about how well he had raised his son: "Charlie was tutored entirely at home and (even leaving out the fact that he is by nature much brighter than I am) is one of the most normal, happy, well-adjusted individuals I have ever seen."[198]

After Dora moved to South Africa, Louis and Carolina got serious about visiting their son and daughter-in-law in America. Charlie suggested two possible travel plans. After taking a passenger ship to New York City, Louis and Carolina could either ride a train across the country to Los Angeles, or they could fly. The train would be comfortable, but slow.

[194] Walker, Chuck, *Atlas: The Ultimate Weapon*, Apogee, 2005.; www.ancestry.com.
[195] "The Atlas Story," *The San Diego Union*, Special Reprint, Feb, 1958.
[196] Martin, Richard E., "The Atlas and Centaur "Steel Balloon" Tanks: A Legacy of Karel Bossart," *AAS History Series, Vol 17*, AAS, San Diego, 1995.
[197] "The Atlas Story," *The San Diego Union*, Feb, 1958.
[198] Letter to Louis, December 19, 1945.

Airline service would get them to California in less than 24 hours, but it would mean taking a series of flights. In those days, airliners flew at a much lower altitude, and the long turbulent rides made many air travelers sick. Louis opted for a variation on the ship-and-train plan.

In August 1946, Charlie's parents boarded a ship from Rotterdam, bound for New Orleans, with stops in the Bahamas and Florida.[199] Louis was fascinated by the technical specifications of the vessel and its engines, writing to Dora at length about its turbines, the steam pressure, etc. Charlie told him to travel light, but Louis brought a box of books to give him something to do once they reached America, a place that he feared might be a cultural wasteland. From New Orleans, they took the Southern Pacific Railroad's "Sunset Route" to Los Angeles. This was still a steam locomotive, which had to make frequent stops for water along the way, but this allowed passengers to visit Pueblo Indian villages and other sights of the Southwest. From his letters, it was clear that they found America more interesting than Louis had anticipated.

Charlie met his parents at the Los Angeles train station. This was a busy period when his work on MX-774 was beginning, but he found time to show them the local culture. They visited San Francisco, where his parents had Chinese food for the first time. They also received their first California sunburn; Louis turned "red as a lobster" after their first day at the beach.

The Bossarts were still living in Norwalk when Louis arrived, but the landlord had informed them earlier in the year that he wanted to move back into his home. It was so difficult to find a rental house that for a time they thought Connie and the children might have to move back to Baltimore temporarily. The eviction happened while Charlie's parents were still visiting; but fortunately he found a new rental property on Clark Avenue in Long Beach, and the landlord was kind enough to help move his furniture.

By this time, they were fed up with the uncertainty of renting houses and wanted to own their home. Connie generally managed the family's finances. Charlie's mind was so immersed in his work, he was barely aware of how much he made in his annual salary.[200] In March 1946, she applied for a $40,000 loan to purchase an acre of avocado groves in Whittier, just up the hill from the "Hacienda" where they had lived two years before. In the post-war economic conversion, it was still difficult to get building materials, so it was not until December that they were able to get a permit.

Now that Charlie had a family of his own, he and his father could debate about the philosophy of child-rearing. Louis had been an extremely

---

[199] Letters from Louis to Dora, May 6, 1946.
[200] Newell and Myrle Ann Bossart, *personal communication*, 2012.

strict parent, but Charlie took a diametrically opposite approach with his children. They ranged from three to seven years old, and the household was noisy and undisciplined by European standards. He never punished them, a task performed solely by Connie, when necessary.[201] He told his wife early on that he wanted his children to grow up to be Americans, not Belgians, and he thought she knew better than he how to make that happen. Louis tried to discipline the children when he first arrived, but Connie let him know in no uncertain terms that policing the behavior of the children was her job. Louis seemed to relax after that, as if relieved of a responsibility that he did not really want.

In a letter to Dora, Louis described a rare moment of peace one evening, when he could collect his thoughts and write. Newell was in bed sick, quietly talking with his grandmother Carolina. Charlie was working in his home office, on something too secret to tell his family about. Connie had taken the other children out to their property in Whittier to pick avocados.[202] It was a respite from what he called "the daily disorder of Karel's family."

Louis was a strict and controlling authority figure, as Charlie and Dora often remarked. But at the same time, he helped his children to develop into confident and formidable people. He gave Charlie a rigorous education, encouraged skepticism and rationality and a love of science and nature. But at the same time, Charlie had more free time and independence than a child spending his days in the school system. Louis sent him to live in France to learn the language and allowed him to work on a transatlantic steamship as a teenager.

In one of their last conversations of the trip, they discussed their differing views on parenting and discipline. Charlie defended his permissive parenting style, and he told his father, "By not teaching our kids respect for authority—not even paternal authority—we Americans believe we can never have any Hitlers or Stalins."[203]

Charlie's parents hadn't meant to stay for four months, but days after their arrival, they were caught in the Great Maritime Strike of 1946. From September to November, the sailors' union and the International Longshoremen's and Warehousemen's Union stopped work at the ports, protesting the economic slowdown after the war. It was not until mid-December that they could find passage on a ship to Europe. Their route

---

[201] Shearer, Lloyd, "Charlie Bossart, Father of the Atlas," *Parade*, March 1, 1959.
[202] Letter from Louis to Dora, Dec 10, 1946.
[203] Letter from Connie and Charlie to Dora, January 17, 1948.

took them through the Panama Canal, one of the engineering marvels of the world, which Louis was excited to see.

The visit to America was the last time Charlie saw his father. Louis Bossart passed away from a heart attack four years later, on December 2, 1950. Charlie flew to Antwerp to attend the funeral and stay with his mother until the end of the month. Dora could not afford the expensive airfare from South Africa and booked passage by ship to visit and comfort her mother. She missed the funeral and got to spend only one day with Charlie, before his return flight to America on New Year's Eve.

At the same time that Charlie's parents were visiting, the Army Air Forces missile project was in full swing. One part of the project was the turbojet cruise missile, code-named MX-774A. They nicknamed it "Teetotaler," because at that time, the largest rockets burned alcohol, but this pilotless aircraft would burn aviation fuel (kerosene). The design was to some extent an unmanned version of the recent XP-92 point-defense fighter, including its butterfly tail and swept-back wings with a 42-foot span. Powered by a pair of Westinghouse jet engines, it would fly 600 miles per hour at an altitude of 45,000 feet, carrying a 5000 pound atomic warhead.[204]

MX-774A was the more conservative part of Convair's proposal, an unmanned airplane, guided to its target by a gyroscopic autopilot or a radio beacon. The responses from the other aircraft companies were all cruise missiles: the Navaho, Matador, Boojum and Snark. To the Air Forces and the aircraft industry, the airplane form of the cruise missile was familiar technology, perceived as cheaper and easier to develop, not something in the realm of science fiction, like rockets. In the war, the German Air Force (Luftwaffe) built over 30,000 of the V-1 flying bombs, five times the number of V-2 rockets built; and the project cost a fraction as much.

The V-1 had a range of 150 to 180 miles, but the Convair cruise missile had a projected range of 4700 miles. To fly such a long distance, with hungry turbojet engines, it had to essentially be a flying fuel tank. Since it was unmanned, they could design a light-weight structure close to the limits of material strength. Charlie permitted load factors of 1.7 to 2.7, much less than the safety standards for a piloted aircraft (typically 6 or 8).[205] The empty aircraft (with engine and warhead) would weigh only 11,650 pounds, and carry 15,450 pounds of fuel—typically the structure of an aircraft was much heavier than the weight of the fuel. One of the weight saving features was a wet-wing fuel tank, that used the sealed skin as the container.

---

[204] *MX-774 Ground to Ground Missile*, CVAC Report 1496-6, October, 1946.
[205] *Monthly Progress Report on MX-774 Ground to Ground Missile*, May, 1946.

Another challenge of long-range flight was the accuracy of the guidance system. A gyroscope suspended in gimbals preserved a fixed reference direction in space, but the vibrations and forces of flight and imperfections of the gyroscope caused the device to slowly drift out of position. Using the existing technology, experts complained that a 5000-mile missile could miss by 75 miles. That was so poor that even an atomic bomb would fail to destroy its target. The foremost authority on gyroscopic guidance was Charles Stark Draper, at MIT, and he estimated that the accuracy of these devices had to be improved by a factor of a thousand.[206]

Charlie was consulting about gyroscopes with Draper, who thought it would take years of research and development to achieve an accuracy of 5000 feet at a distance of 5000 miles. To complete development sooner, Charlie had to consider other guidance technologies. The tracking problem for cruise missiles was two-dimensional, guiding the vehicle to its target over the surface of the Earth. His electronics expert Jim Crooks proposed a long-range radio guidance system they called Hypergrid, based on the concepts of LORAN (a radio navigation system developed by the Army Signal Corps in the early 1940s). Two very low frequency (40-200 kHz) radio signals would be sent from stations hundreds of miles apart, and the missile would follow a path of constant phase difference.[207]

In November of 1946, Charlie's team began testing a scaled-down version of Hypergrid, using a shorter wavelength (150 MHz). In San Diego, they set up two stations a few miles apart, at Convair's Radio and Electrical Lab and on Mt. Soledad. The receiver system was installed in a Curtiss C-46 transport plane supplied by the Air Forces. Spread out across a long table in the cargo hold were radio receivers, a phase-comparison unit, and servo amplifiers. The airplane's autopilot was designed to maintain a steady course and altitude, but it had a rudder control input that could execute flat turns, and this was coupled to the Hypergrid prototype. With this setup, they made a number of automatically guided flights from San Diego to the naval air base at Point Mugu, 139 miles away.[208]

Radio jamming was a potential problem for Hypergrid, so as a backup the team also developed the Automatic Magnetic Guidance System, where the missile would follow paths of constant intensity of the Earth's magnetic field. A prototype of that system was also flight tested successfully on the C-46. For the sensor, they adapted an ultra-sensitive magnetometer used for submarine detection.

---

[206] Mackenzie, Donald, "Inventing Accuracy," MIT 1990.
[207] *MX-774 Ground to Ground Missile: Summary Report*, CVAC Report, December, 1949.
[208] MX-774 Ground-to-Ground Missile, Summary Report, December 1, 1949.

However, work on the cruise missile project was short lived. After the war, the mood of the country was conservative and frugal. Policy makers were complacent about American security, because they had the largest navy and air force in the world. In addition, the United States was the only nation with the atomic bomb, and Convair's B-36 bomber seemed to be an adequate long-range delivery system. The forward-looking General Hap Arnold retired in early 1946, and the new leadership was not as committed to what they viewed as futuristic technologies. In December, the budget for the Air Force's experimental-missile program was drastically cut, from $29 to $13 million, and eleven research projects were halted.[209] Among them, Convair's MX-774A cruise missile was cancelled in favor of Northrop's Snark. Along with it, work on the Hypergrid and magnetic guidance systems came to an end.

Privately, Charlie was glad they did not have to spend more time on the cruise-missile concept. He favored ballistic rockets, because he was worried that air defense technology would become too good for aircraft to penetrate Russian air space (by this time, relations with the Soviet Union had soured). As he later said, "We thought the reason for going to a long-range missile like that, instead of a bomber, was that a bomber could not get through. We didn't think an air-breathing job would get through any better than a bomber."[210]

Germany had already carried out the experiment of cruise missile versus ballistic missile, and Charlie was very familiar with the result. He had a special interest, since both V-weapons had been directed against his home city of Antwerp, and he got the inside story about Allied air-defense systems from his team member, Bill Patterson. When V-1s began striking London in June of 1944, conventional defenses (flak guns and barrage balloons) were somewhat overwhelmed. However, the buzz bombs were in trouble after the arrival of American radar-controlled guns, installed on the coast of Britain (where Patterson captained a unit) and around Antwerp.[211]

The American anti-aircraft batteries used a coordinated system of new technologies. Based on servo-control research at MIT, the SCR-584 was the first radar that could lock onto and track a target automatically. The target's trajectory information was fed by the radar into an M-9 analog computer, developed at Bell Laboratories. Calculating how much to lead the target and compensate for the shell's drop in elevation during flight, the M-9 sent

---

[209] Beard, Edmund, *Developing the ICBM*, Columbia Univ. Press, NY, 1976.; Rosenberg, Max, *The Air Force and the National guided Missile Program: 1944-1950*, Lion Publications, 2012.

[210] "Bossart Wins M/R Goddard Trophy," *Missiles and Rockets*, Feb 15, 1960. (By "air-breathing" he was referring to jet engines, as opposed to rockets, which carry their own oxygen supply).

[211] Patterson, William H., *The Evolution of a New Technology Concept in the U.S.A.*, 1985.

instructions to four motor-controlled 90mm cannons. They were armed with radio-proximity shells that would detonate when they sensed the metal body of a V-1. This set of inventions hinted at the electronics revolution brewing in the United States. Their smooth orchestration into one military system demonstrated a new methodology for developing complex technology, which Americans called Systems Engineering.

Along the lanes of incoming V-1s, fifty of these advanced gun batteries were deployed around Antwerp. Firing on the cruise missiles more rapidly and accurately than manually operated guns, only 211 got through to the port, while over 2000 were shot down.[212]

At the very least, that was the level of anti-aircraft technology an intercontinental cruise missile would face. The Soviet Union had been given SCR-584 radars during the war, and they began to manufacture their own copies of it. Furthermore, since Charlie had worked on Lark and Bumblebee, he knew that radar-guided and heat-seeking anti-aircraft missiles were the next stage of air-defense technology.

In contrast to the vulnerable V-1, the V-2 ballistic missile had been unstoppable. It flew through the ionosphere and descended upon its targets at supersonic speed. It was simply impossible to shoot a vehicle traveling at that speed and coming in from such high altitude.

The second part of Convair's proposal was the supersonic intercontinental ballistic missile; code-named MX-774B and nicknamed "Manhattan," in reference to the project that developed the atomic bomb.

Up until then, the most powerful rocket in the world was the V-2, but it was now viewed as a short-range missile. In early 1946, the team had not yet received many details about the V-2 from the Army. They studied photos in a Life Magazine article to get some idea of its size and shape.[213] But Charlie liked to start from first principles when he tackled a problem, and he took their ignorance about the German rocket as a blessing. He later explained, "In the first few months, we came up with a whole set of fresh concepts about missiles. There were no precedents or traditions to hamper us."[214]

Missiles traveled in a manner more akin to an artillery shell than an aircraft. It was popular to imagine a rocket traveling like an arrow through space, with engines blazing. However, the reality was more like a ballistic

[212] Backus, R.J., *The Defense of Antwerp Against the V-1 Missiles*, Southern Colorado State College Thesis, 1965.; Hamilton, John A., "Cruise Missile Defense: Defending Antwerp against the V-1," *Fires Bulletin*, January, 2008.
[213] "U.S. Tests Rockets In New Mexico," *Life*, May 27, 1946.
[214] Shearer, Lloyd, "Charlie Bossart, Father of the Atlas," *Parade*, March 1, 1959.

projectile. An intercontinental rocket burned all of its fuel in the first few hundred miles during a boost phase that lasted several minutes. After that, it tumbled through space, on an unpowered trajectory that was determined only by the laws of gravity and inertia. As it approached its destination, it would plunge into the atmosphere and detonate above the target. This presented three major technical challenges: developing the power to go that far, devising an accurate guidance system, and surviving the heat of reentering the atmosphere at meteoric speed.

A missile's range depended on how fast it could go before engine shutdown, analogous to the muzzle velocity of a cannon. The V-2 missile accelerated to 3600 mph; but to achieve intercontinental distance, the ICBM had to reach 16,000 miles per hour, close to the velocity needed to enter orbit.

In 1903, Tsiolkovsky proved that two factors determined a rocket's maximum velocity: the rocket-engine exhaust speed, and the ratio of fuel mass to structure mass.[215] Charlie's team would have to work on both factors to meet the range requirement.

Exhaust velocity is increased primarily by using more energetic fuels to raise the temperature in the combustion chamber. But high temperature is itself a problem. Burning fuel under pressure in pure oxygen could melt the combustion chamber or burn a hole in it. On the V-2 project, German engineers had first tried using the inflowing propellant to cool the chamber walls. But the thick steel did not conduct heat fast enough to prevent the inner surface from overheating. To get the cooling they needed, they borrowed an idea from Robert Goddard's patents, seeping fuel through small pores on the inside of the combustion chamber. Even after those measures were taken, it was necessary to add water to the fuel to lower the temperature of combustion.[216] Thus, the V-2 achieved an exhaust velocity of only 7600 feet/sec.

Charlie knew that the rocket engine's exhaust velocity was the most influential factor in the missile's performance. The Vultee Field group had designed and tested small rocket engines during the XP-92 project, but the problem of engine design became more difficult as the size and power increased. For expert advice, they reached out to Aerojet Engineering, von Kármán's company in nearby Pasadena.

For the Manhattan missile, Charlie's first plan was a relatively small rocket, only 50 feet long and 5 feet in diameter. He designed a 4100-pound

---

[215] Tsiolkovsky, "Issledovanie Mirovykh Prostranstv Reaktivnymi Priborami," *Vestnik Vozdukhoplavaniya*," *Nauchnoe Obozrenie* (5), pp. 45-75, May 1903. ("The Investigation of Outer Space with Rocket Devices")

[216] The V-2 burned a mix of 75% ethyl alcohol and 25% water.

airframe that was lighter than the V-2, but it would hold 50% more fuel. In terms of Tsiolkovsky's performance factors, the Manhattan's design had twice the mass ratio of the German rocket; but to get the required range, he also needed to double the engine exhaust speed.

A radical increase in exhaust velocity could be achieved by using exotic super fuels. The first plan for MX-774B was to burn liquid hydrogen with liquid fluorine, giving an exhaust speed of 15,000 feet/sec. This was the highest performance that Aerojet engineers thought possible using any combination of chemicals.[217] However, they cautioned Charlie that fluorine was extremely poisonous and corrosive, and liquid hydrogen was so cold (-423° F) that there was little experience with handling and storing it. No engine existed that could contain such a high-energy chemical reaction. On a more practical note, Aerojet's theorists were confident that 11,000 feet/sec exhaust could be achieved without resorting to dangerous or super-cold propellants. What was needed was a better engine design that could handle higher chamber pressures and sensible propellants, such as liquid oxygen and kerosene.

Anyone who had a fresh idea was welcome in Charlie's group, and one of the most unusual was the idea to study triatomic hydrogen H_3 as a fuel.[218] In theory it would yield a fantastically high exhaust speed, considerably more than ordinary diatomic hydrogen H_2. However, chemists and physicists had spent decades arguing about whether or not triatomic hydrogen even existed.[219] Opinions on this controversial substance ranged from theoretical proofs that it could not exist to reports of synthesis and measurements of its boiling point. Charlie was willing to take a risk, as long as experiments validated the idea. In May of 1946, he authorized a small lab-bench project to repeat a published synthesis technique. In a manner similar to how ozone (O_3) is generated, hydrogen was passed through an electric arc and then into a cold condensation trap. But the experiment failed to produce results. Today, it is known that triatomic hydrogen is unstable (the H_3 molecule decomposes in less than a microsecond).

As the use of super fuels became more unlikely, the hope for a 50-foot ICBM faded. Hope vanished entirely when the payload was increased from 2200 to 6000 pounds. The new plan was for MX-774B to carry the W-4 warhead, which contained a fission bomb with a 31-kiloton yield.

---

[217] *MX-774 Ground to Ground Missile*, CVAC Report 1496-1, May, 1946.
[218] *MX-774 Ground to Ground Missile: Summary Report*, CVAC Report, December, 1949.
[219] Kragh, Helge, "A Controversial Molecule: The Early History of Triatomic Hydrogen," *Cenaurus*, 2011.

Tsiolkovsky's second factor of rocket performance was about reducing the mass of the rocket structure, which was Charlie's specialty. "Saving structural weight was like second nature to me," he later wrote.[220] A rocket should have the highest possible mass ratio: the weight of the propellant divided by the weight of the empty rocket. It was becoming clear that MX-774B was going to be a large rocket, and it would have to push the limits of science and engineering. As Charlie later wrote, "If structural materials were just a little less strong, if the energy content of fuels were just a little less, if the pull of gravity were just a little higher, the job couldn't be done at all."[221]

When Charlie was optimizing the weight of the Teetotaler cruise missile, the problem was challenging but relatively familiar. For an aircraft, there was a standard procedure: the stresses were calculated in level flight, and then the aircraft design was strengthened further by load factors, to survive extraordinary maneuvers and wind conditions.

When they focused their attention on the supersonic Manhattan rocket, Charlie and his weights engineer Cleon Holden knew they were in uncharted territory. There was no guide book of load factors for a missile that would go three times as fast as the V-2. What would the stresses be during nominal flight? What were the extraordinary conditions created by air friction, intense acceleration and guidance-control maneuvers? The speeds and atmospheric conditions at high altitude were beyond what they could test in their wind tunnels. And all these questions had to be answered precisely, because strength and weights had to be designed close to the failure point. In Charlie's words, "You kid yourself right out of the picture if you don't guess your weights correctly on a long-range missile."[222]

Charlie was convinced that they needed to build and fly a test missile to study the structural requirements of an ICBM. The Army Air Forces agreed and in June of 1946, they kicked in an extra $493,000 to cover the development cost of a set of test rockets, code named RTV-A-2.[223] Its nickname was "Old Fashioned" because of the superficial resemblance to the V-2. In the first months of the project, the team learned a little about the German missile, but internally, their test rocket was not very similar. They already had a lot of new ideas, and they were bringing the knowledge and style of modern aircraft design to the problem.

As he learned more details of the V-2 construction, Charlie was surprised by how heavily overbuilt it was, with steel skin over a load-bearing

---

[220] Bossart, Karel J., Letter to Herbert F. York, January, 1974.

[221] Bossart, K.J., "Some facts about rockets," *Het Ingenieursblad*, 34(5), 1965.

[222] Chapman, John L., *Atlas: The Story of a Missile*, Harper, New York, 1960.

[223] The RTV-A-2 test rocket is often referred to as the MX-774, but strictly speaking, that was the code name for the ICBM. RTV-A-2 stood for "Research Test Vehicle – Air Force - #2".

framework of rings and longitudinal rails. It did not provide good insight into load factors, because its design was so conservative. Adding to the weight, it contained separate aluminum propellant tanks inside the hull, and the liquid oxygen tank was insulated with fiberglass. The V-2 central section (excluding nose cone and engine sections) weighted 1635 pounds and held 19,200 pounds of propellant: a mass ratio of 11.7.

Charlie designed the central section of RTV-A-2 as a monocoque hull, with no internal framework. Instead of steel, he used 6061 aluminum.[224] This was a weldable alloy (unlike duralumin), making it easy to use the skin of the rocket as a sealed tank for the propellants (instead of a "wet wing," he had a "wet fuselage"). The forward instrument section and aft engine compartment were made from riveted duralumin, which had greater strength. Charlie saved some more weight when experiments demonstrated that insulating the liquid oxygen tank was unnecessary. The central section of the test missile weighed only 89 pounds and held 3000 pounds of propellant. The mass ratio was 33.7, which was three times better than the V-2.

In May, even before the test-missile was officially approved, the MX-774 team began meeting with Reaction Motors Inc. (RMI), the company that had built the engines for the Lark missile. RMI was formed in 1941, by James H. Wyld and several other members of the American Rocket Society. In 1938, Wyld had developed a robust rocket engine that used regenerative cooling—fuel flowed around the walls, absorbing heat before entering the combustion chamber. It was remarkable, because rocket engines that ran for even a couple minutes without melting were unusual in the 1930s.

Wyld's three-ton thrust 6000-C4 engine was used in the X-1 rocket plane, the first manned aircraft to break the speed of sound. For the MX-774 test rocket, RMI improved the X-1 engine, producing the 8000-C4. The thrust was boosted to four tons by burning more concentrated alcohol (95%) at a higher chamber pressure. More important than the higher thrust was an increase in exhaust speed, from 6700 to 7300 feet/sec. The turbine fuel pump was based on a design by Robert Goddard.

One of Charlie's design innovations was to steer the rocket by swiveling the engines. The V-2 was steered by graphite vanes poking into the exhaust stream, but that reduced the thrust. At Convair's request, the 8000-C4 chambers were hinge-mounted to pivot ±10 degrees on one axis. By moving the four chambers independently, the guidance system could turn the rocket in any direction. Looking at the engine from the bottom, the

---

[224] *MX-774 Ground to Ground Missile*, CVAC Report 1496-6, October, 1946. The test rocket could stand up without pressurization, unlike the radically thin "balloon" design of the Atlas.

two chambers at 12 o'clock and 6 o'clock could pivot to the left or right to adjust yaw. The chambers at 3 o'clock and 9 o'clock could pivot up and down to change the pitch. All four chambers could pivot clockwise or counter-clockwise to roll the rocket about its axis.[225]

Charlie's assistant, Lloyd Standley, designed the hydraulic actuators that pivoted the engine chambers. He worked with RMI at their plant in New Jersey during the course of these modifications. Two clever weight-saving scheme were to use the pressurized fuel as the hydraulic fluid and to use the tank pressurization gas to operate pneumatic valves.

The RTV-A-2 was guided by a gyroscopic system. As a boy, Charlie had seen a trained seal balance a ball on its nose, keeping its snout precisely aligned below the ball's center of gravity. He compared the seal's strategy to the rocket's steering and control system, pointing the engines to keep the missile upright, and putting it into a predicted trajectory.[226]

Accuracy was not the only technical problem in guidance systems. It took several decades to discover how to properly use the information from a gyroscope to implement stable motion control. Robert Goddard was the first to use a gyro in a rocket, in 1932. But not being an expert on control systems, his rockets had a problem. As they rose into the air, attempting to maintain a vertical course, his rockets snaked from side to side, correcting the course, overshooting and then correcting in the opposite direction.

The oscillating behavior of Goddard's rockets was called "hunting," and it was noticed centuries ago in the steering of large ships. A human pilot trying to follow a compass bearing would inevitably zig-zag along the intended path, as he corrected one way and then the other. Not following a straight line (the shortest distance between two points) meant that ships wasted time and fuel, but it was only when the Sperry gyro-pilot system was introduced that the problem was fixed. For many years, the method of preventing hunting was a closely guarded trade secret, but in the 1920s, engineers had a good understanding of so-called control theory. The key idea was to calculate course corrections, not just from the deviation, but also from the rate (speed) of deviation.[227] Essentially, the rate signal simulated the action of friction, which damped out the oscillations of hunting.

For autopilots and guidance systems, specialized gyroscopes were used to measure course deviation and the rate of deviation. The V-2 guidance

---

[225] An easy way to remember yaw, pitch and roll is this: when you steer your car to the left or right, you are changing the yaw. Driving up and down a hill, your car is changing pitch. When a plane or car banks, it is making a roll maneuver, rotating around the axis of the direction of travel.

[226] *The General Dynamics Astronautics Story*, [vinyl record], 1963.

[227] Bennett, S., *A History of Control Engineering: 1800-1930*, IET Publications, 1986.

system was built by Siemens Corporation. There engineers were familiar with the theory of control, and the first guidance-system designs used direction and rate gyros. However, war-time shortages of parts prevented them from mass producing an ideal guidance system. Instead, they used only direction gyros and approximated the rate signal with a circuit that differentiated the direction signal. It was clever but not very accurate.

For the gyro guidance system of his test rocket, Charlie tried to get copies of the unit used by the Army's Corporal E missile. It was developed in 1944 by Sperry Gyroscope Co., but they declined to build copies for Convair. So the team designed their own, assembled from standard aviation instruments. Three direction gyros, from a Bendex Fluxgate compass, measured yaw, pitch and roll angles. Three rate gyros, from bank-and-turn indicators, measured the rocket's rotational velocity. It was actually more sophisticated than the guidance system of the Corporal.[228] Amplifiers mixed the direction and rate information and controlled the hydraulic system that pivoted the engine chambers.

The test rocket was a highly original design, but they copied one feature of the V-2: the shape of the fins.[229] The V-2 had an unusual truncated fin with a vertical outer edge. Copying the design allowed them to use V-2 wind tunnel data for aerodynamics and stress analysis, but they never understood why the Germans had chosen that shape. In October, 1946, three German experts, Hermann, Goethert and Lippisch, visited Convair to consult on supersonic aerodynamics for the XP-92 delta fighter and the MX-774 missile.[230] Charlie asked about the scientific reason for the V-2 fin design, and Dr. Hermann laughed, explaining that the tips of triangular fins had been chopped off so the missile could fit through railroad tunnels.

By fall of 1946, design drawings had been sent to the workshops, where the test missiles were being built. In February, Bill Patterson did tests of the aerodynamic stability of scale models, in Convair's four-foot wind tunnel. The rocket was expected to reach a top speed of Mach 4.4, so he also tested it in the supersonic wind tunnel at the Army's Ballistic Research Lab in Aberdeen. The rocket engines had been purchased from RMI, to be delivered in March.[231]

[228] MX-774 Ground to Ground Missile, CVAC Report 1496-6, October, 1946.
[229] Chapman, John L., *Atlas: The Story of a Missile*, Harper, New York, 1960.
[230] Rudolf Hermann ran the supersonic wind tunnel at Peenemünde, Bernhard Goethert was head of high speed aerodynamics at the Berlin Research Institute of Aerodynamics, and Alexander Lippisch was an advocate of swept-wing designs at the Vienna Aerodynamics Institute.
[231] MX-774 Ground to Ground Missile, CVAC Report 1496-6, October, 1946.

For the Manhattan missile, MX-774B, the gyro guidance system of the test rocket was nowhere near sophisticated enough. The accuracy specification for Manhattan was equivalent to throwing a basketball a mile and having it land in the hoop. Once the ball leaves the player's hands, its course is completely determined; and similarly, when the rocket completed its short boost phase, its direction and speed had to be exact. The guidance problem was different from the cruise missile. Rather than maintain a stable course for hours, it had to be extraordinarily accurate during the few minutes of rocket-powered thrust. It would be a decade before Prof. Draper's team at MIT would perfect gyroscope technology to the necessary level of accuracy.

Once again, Charlie turned to his resident electronics genius, Jim Crooks, to design a radio-based guidance system for the Manhattan. The problem was more complex than for the Teetotaler. For the cruise missile, the hypergrid radio system had to provide only compass bearing (azimuth); but for a ballistic missile, the azimuth and elevation angles and speed all had to be measured. Their first idea was to use a radio system developed for the Army's Corporal missile: three SCR-584 radar ground stations to track and triangulate the missile. But after considering that plan, Crooks proposed a new more elegant solution that would use a single ground station.

Crooks worked with Robert Weaver at the Convair Radio and Electrical Lab in San Diego. Crooks and Weaver planned to use radio phase comparison to measure direction angles with an accuracy of $1/10,000^{th}$ of a degree. A radio range finding system would measure distance, and Doppler radar could measure the missile's velocity. A computer would combine all of this information and transmit radio commands to the missile, adjusting its trajectory and shutting off the engine when it reached the required speed.

Crooks planned to use microwaves (5 GHz) to get the most accurate measurements. Microwave electronics was a new and difficult technology in those days, so for testing purposes he built a VHF (150 MHz) version. It just measured azimuth angle with an accuracy of about 2 degrees, testing one dimension of the angle finder (the production system would use two angle finders to measure azimuth and elevation). A VHF range finder and a Doppler speedometer system were also developed. An array of antennas with a 200 foot baseline was installed on Mt. Soledad, in San Diego. In July of 1947, ground tests were made, tracking a cart 12.5 miles away at Lindbergh Field. Using a C-46, three flight tests were made in December and January.

A successful flight was made 139 miles to the Point Mugu air base. The plane's bearing was measured and controlled by radio commands from Mt.

Soledad that controlled the plane's autopilot. But when the C-46 reached Point Mugu, the ground crew, assigned to spot the plane, was eating lunch. As he flew by, the pilot made an estimate that they passed 800 feet from the runway, which was the accuracy expected.[232]

The precision radio guidance system was given its name by a Convair manager during a meeting with contractors. He was forced to come up with something on the spur of the moment, and he called it "Azusa," a Southern California town made famous by a long-running gag on the Jack Benny show.[233] The microwave version took a few years to complete and was not ready in time for use on the test missile project, but it was used extensively by NASA at Cape Canaveral. Once developed, Azusa had twice the accuracy of existing radar tracking systems.[234]

One more new problem was associated with an intercontinental rocket. After coasting through space for half an hour, the missile would dive back into the atmosphere like a meteor over the target. Unlike previous experience with short-range rockets, the reentry velocity of an ICBM was over 16,000 mph, more than twenty times the speed of sound. An object plunging into the atmosphere at such speed creates a shockwave in front of it, and the air is compressed so violently that it becomes incandescent. Even solid rock was vaporized.

Earlier missiles like the V-2 did not go far enough (and therefore not fast enough) to suffer from reentry heating, but they still had problems. The V-2 had been designed to reenter the atmosphere as a whole, so after tumbling through the ionosphere its fins would orient it nose-first during its final approach. This required the rocket to be strong enough to withstand the aerodynamic load, which was part of why they were so overbuilt and heavy. And even then, many of them broke apart, a phenomenon the Germans called *Luftzerleger* ("air burst").

In the MX-774, Charlie solved this problem by ejecting the nose cone in flight, so only the warhead section needed to be strong enough for atmospheric reentry. It was going to be difficult enough to build a nose cone that could withstand the tremendous aerodynamic loads and the intense heat, and nobody wanted to design a heavily reinforced rocket that could survive those conditions. Although it did not travel nearly as far or fast, the RTV-A-2 would test the concept by ejecting the five-foot cover of

[232] *MX-774 Ground to Ground Missile: Summary Report*, CVAC Report, December, 1949.; Chapman, John L., *Atlas: The Story of a Missile*, Harper, New York, 1960.

[233] Mel Blanc, "Train leaving on track five for Anaheim, Azusa and Cucamonga!"

[234] Neufeld, Jacob, *The Development of Ballistic Missiles in the United States Air Force, 1945-1960*, Office of Air Force History, Washington, 1990.

the nose section. That would release a 40-foot parachute so the rest of the rocket would fall slowly enough to be recovered.

The thermal problem of reentry was daunting. Their first thought was to use a heat-resistant substance, and they consulted with Norton Abrasives about materials such as graphite, alumina and magnorite.[235] For example, magnorite (magnesium oxide) melts at 5166° F. However, they quickly realized that reentry temperatures were beyond what any material could withstand. They calculated the warhead would be exposed to temperatures hotter than the surface of the sun, from 9000 to 30,000° F.

To help study the thermodynamics and aerodynamics of high-speed reentry, they hired Professor Karl Dawson Wood, from the University of Colorado. Charlie assumed that the warhead should be a pointed streamlined shape, like a supersonic aircraft. But in July of 1947, Prof. Wood reported something surprising. His calculations showed that a spherical reentry vehicle was ideal. It would slow down rapidly and be exposed to high temperatures for a shorter duration of time.[236]

Their new plan was to house the warhead inside a spherical steel heatsink that would simply absorb the thermal energy of reentry. Wood's calculations showed that the outer half inch would be melted, but the warhead would survive. The idea of the blunt reentry body is generally attributed to H. Julian Allen, a researcher at Ames Research Center. In 1952, Allen suggested that a sphere, "like an old Civil War cannonball" would be an optimal shape.[237] Wood's earlier discovery of this idea was only published in classified Convair reports, so he never got credit.

In July of 1947, the ICBM project was interrupted by Convair's decision to close down Vultee Field, sell the facility to North American Aviation, and move the operations to San Diego.

The move to San Diego was inconvenient for Charlie. On his property in Whittier, the foundation of their new home was complete, and his contractor convinced them to finish the house and sell it. Designed by the architect Max Mason Jr., it was located on a steep hillside, presenting a one-story front on South Circle Drive and two stories in the rear. The interior was paneled in Douglas fir and redwood, but the Bossart family was never able to live in their dream home. Construction was not finished until the fall of 1947, and it took a few years to find a buyer for the property. In the

---

[235] MX-774 Ground-to-Ground Missile, CVAC Report 1496-6, October, 1946.

[236] MX-774 Ground-to-0round Missile, Summary Report, December, 1949.

[237] Vincenti, Boyd and Bugos, "H. Julian Allen: An Appreciation," *Annual Rev. Fluid Mech.,* 2007.

meantime, they helped their finances by selling about 5000 pounds of avocados from the orchard every year.[238]

Like the rest of the Los Angeles operation, the MX-774 project moved in July. Parts were lost, drawings were lost, and some personnel quit rather than move. North American Aviation made a handsome job offer for Charlie to stay and work for them in Whittier, but he was committed to working on his missile project.[239] For some months Charlie was able to spend only weekends with his family. Connie and the children did not move down to San Diego until November.

San Diego was a Navy town, hosting the largest base on the West Coast, but it was also the headquarters of Consolidated Aircraft Corporation. During the war, their plants built B-24 bombers and employed 45,000 people, but this dropped to fewer than 4000 jobs, as defense spending ramped down after 1945.[240] It was a blow to the city's economy. No one could have foreseen that the imagination and perseverance of one man would result in a major new missile business that would be part of the city's recovery.

In San Diego, the Bossart family rented a house in Lemon Grove for two years and then settled into a home on Missouri Street in Pacific Beach. It was a working-class neighborhood; and as always, they made friends quickly. Connie helped care for neighbors' children when both parents had to work during the day. Her friends called her "Mrs. B." Charlie's new office in San Diego was at the administrative headquarters of Convair, a massive windowless concrete building known to everyone as "The Rock."[241] Across the highway from it was the sprawling complex of aircraft Plant No. 1, and beyond that the Lindbergh Field Airport. Half a mile from his office was the site of the former factory of Ryan Airlines, where Charlie had first visited San Diego in 1926.

The same month that Vultee Field was closed, Charlie got more bad news. In a new round of spending cuts, the Army Air Forces cancelled the MX-774 project. In the 5000-mile range category, only the Snark cruise missile remained. The Air Forces brass concluded that long-range rockets did not promise tangible results in less than ten years.

One of the technical reasons for cancellation of the Manhattan rocket was concern that the necessary exhaust speed could not be reached with conventional fuels (liquid oxygen and alcohol). Another issue cited in the

---

[238] Letter to his parents, February 12, 1950.
[239] "The Atlas Story," *The San Diego Union*, Feb, 1958.; Letter to parents, July 6, 1947.
[240] Pescador and Aldrich, *Consolidated Aircraft Corporation*, SASM, 2008.
[241] Today it is the headquarters building for the Port of San Diego.

cancellation order was the reentry problem. To make matters worse, presidential science advisor, MIT professor Vannevar Bush, had denounced the idea of the intercontinental rocket. In December 1945, he told Congress, "I take very little stock indeed in the continent-to-continent missile, in spite of some of the unfortunate publicity that was given to it soon after the end of the war. I think these things will be just too expensive and too inaccurate to use, even if they could be built."

The decision to cancel MX-774 would later be judged as short-sighted. A decade later, when Sputnik was launched by the Soviet Union, generals and scientists would be called to testify before Congress about why America dropped the ball on long-range rockets. The Atlas was completed the same year as the Soviet ICBM, but the U.S.A. lost a lot of potential development time.

Charlie and his team remained convinced that a ballistic missile was needed, and that cruise missiles would be shot down by anti-aircraft defenses. He talked the Air Forces into letting them build the RTV-A-2 test missiles. He had hoped to make ten rockets of varying size, and then a two-stage test rocket with a range of 1300 miles. Instead, they received permission and funding to build three single-stage rockets. Convair tried to get additional funding of $1.5 million to build 15 of the test rockets as high-altitude scientific rockets, but this plan ran afoul of rivalry with the Navy's Viking rocket. Competition among the Army, Army Air Forces and Navy over scarce funding for rocket research contributed to the difficulty of developing the ICBM.[242]

After the war, the company had to consider how to maintain its large operation in the post-war economy. The B-36 intercontinental bomber contract was not enough, and the company wanted to get into civilian airliner business. Douglas, Lockheed and Boeing dominated the market for large planes, but Convair saw opportunity in medium-size airliners. After $32 million in development costs ($390 million in 2016 dollars), they flew the prototype of the 40-passenger Convair 240 in July of 1946. Martin Aircraft Co. also entered that market, and competition with them kept prices low and made it difficult for Convair to recover the massive amount of money they had spent on developing the airliner and retooling for its production.[243] Thus in 1947, Convair was in serious financial trouble.

In the fall of 1947, Convair Corporation was rescued by a new owner. Floyd Odlum was one of the richest men in America, and he had a personal

[242] Beard, Edmund, *Developing the ICBM*, Columbia Univ. Press, NY, 1976. The Viking rocket (RTV-N-12) was based on a Reaction Motors engine, which was a copy of the German Wasserfall anti-aircraft-missile engine.

[243] Wilson, Gill Robb, "Convair: Industrial Giant of the Air Age," *Flying Magazine*, Jul-Oct, 1960.

love of aviation. His wife was Jacqueline Cochran, a famous aviator who helped found the Women's Air Corps (WAC). She later became the first female pilot in the world to break the sound barrier. Odlum began buying up stock in AVCO, Victor Emanuel's holding company which owned Convair. In September Emanuel agreed to exchange Convair Corporation for Odlum's AVCO stock and in November, Odlum took executive control. The influx of new money allowed the company to hold out until sales of their plane could bring in revenue. In two years, he returned the company to profitability. The CV-240 airliner went on to become a work horse of the airline industry, and Convair sold over a thousand of them.

With the company cutting costs, the future of rocket research was very much in question. However, Charlie's team had "the inspiration of missionaries," as he later said. Odlum met with Charlie and agreed with him that the government would someday realize that it needed an ICBM. Defying the board of directors, he authorized the team to continue working on designs and theoretical studies. By the time government funding for Atlas was authorized, Convair had spent $3 million and allocated 15,000 engineering man-hours to long-range rocket studies.[244]

Their customer for the missile was the Air Force R&D organization at Wright-Patterson Air Force Base, the Air Material Command (after 1951, the Air Research & Development Command).[245] Charlie and Bill Patterson made many trips to Wright Field and Washington D.C., explaining their ideas and asking for funding. Over time, lobbying became Patterson's primary job. They found some sympathetic supporters, but many generals considered an intercontinental rocket to be science fiction, or so advanced that it would take decades to perfect.

Not all of Charlie's difficulties in promoting the ICBM were due to serious political and military disagreements. One important meeting with Pentagon brass was scuttled when a model of their proposed missile could not be removed from a massively overbuilt shipping crate.[246] On another trip, he was so preoccupied with work that he flew to Washington without his partial dentures (he had lost some teeth in an accident during his youth). He telephoned Connie, and the airline graciously sent his false teeth on the next cross-country flight.

Work on the RTV-A-2 test missile resumed as soon as Charlie's team was settled in their new San Diego offices. The next step was static testing—

---

[244] Dunne, Vincent, "Atlas 10-Year Gamble That Won", *Evening Tribune*, San Diego, May 4, 1956.
[245] In 1947, the Army Air Forces became the U.S. Air Force, independent of the Army.
[246] Pearson, Drew, "Big Businessmen Deserve Credit For Mercury Orbit," *Washington Merry-Go-Round*, Mar 9, 1962.

firing a rocket in a stand without letting it fly. They scouted out a suitable location on the remote western shore of Point Loma peninsula, near the Navy Electronics Laboratory and out of sight from San Diego. During the war, the property had been the site of a coastal artillery emplacement. By August of 1947, a test stand was built from a 70-foot oil derrick, rigged to suspend the 30-foot rocket in a gimbal and turntable. This would allow the steering system to yaw, pitch or roll the rocket and test its ability to stabilize the rocket.[247] A water jet installed on the concrete pad could cool the engine after it was shut down or put out a fire in case of an emergency. One hundred fifty feet away, a blockhouse for control and observation was erected and armored with sand bags.

The first static firing was scheduled for November 20, but Lloyd Standley found problems with the electric igniters.[248] The four combustion chambers of the 8000-C4 engine had to start simultaneously with pyrotechnic squibs—electric filaments running through a cartridge of slow burning flash powder, something like Fourth-of-July sparklers. Standley took some squibs home with him and carefully cleaned and rebuilt them. Starting a rocket engine had to be done with care. The worst case scenario was a "hard start," when ignition is done too late, and the combustion chamber is flooded with propellant mixture and explodes.

The next morning, the rocket was ready for testing. A Navy guard stationed himself on the road entering the site, in case tourists tried to drive into the area while the secret operation was underway. 196 gallons of alcohol was pumped into the rocket from drums, and then a specialized truck delivered 167 gallons of liquid oxygen. The last and most treacherous of the propellants was the concentrated hydrogen peroxide, which could decompose explosively if mishandled. The peroxide was used to power the turbine fuel pumps. Nick Keough, the test supervisor, was the last man off the firing stand. He threw the safety switch that enabled ignition, and just for fun, he rode the emergency zip-line from the top of the derrick to the blockhouse.[249]

At 11:30, the firing button was pushed. As the test team looked on, and movie cameras photographed the test stand, the turbo pump spun up, fuel pressure climbed, and the squibs were triggered. Charlie saw two jets of flame emerge from the bottom of the rocket...but there should have been four. Three seconds after ignition, there was an explosion in the engine section and flames billowed all the way to the top of the derrick. At six

---

[247] Chapman, John L., *Atlas: The Story of a Missile*, Harper, New York, 1960.

[248] MX-774 Ground to Ground Missile, CVAC Report 1496-14, December, 1947.

[249] Chapman, John L., *Atlas: The Story of a Missile*, Harper, New York, 1960. (He's also seen riding the zip-line in a video of the test).

seconds, someone was able to throw the emergency cutoff switch and turned on the water jet. [250]

Once the fire was extinguished, the crew had to wait near the blockhouse. No liquid oxygen (often abbreviated "LOX") could be seen venting, and there was concern that it might boil and explode the tanks. The Navy guard offered to release the pressure by shooting a hole in the tank, but they decided to wait for one hour. When it was finally deemed safe to approach the wrecked missile, they discovered the LOX had all leaked out through a ruptured feed line.

After some analysis, they realized that two of the squibs had failed to go off. Those two chambers had filled with propellant until detonated by the exhaust flames from the two working chambers. The engines and some of the rocket structure were mangled, but the water jet saved the rocket from being entirely destroyed. At least they got some telemetry data, and many systems functioned normally. Like many failed tests, the results were not completely without value. The Air Force gave Convair an additional $250,000 to repair the damaged rocket and continue testing.

In January, the next static test went perfectly. All four engine chambers started and ran for the planned 35 seconds. For the next few firings, the rocket was locked immobile in the test stand, so the engine system could be tested. After that, the rocket was allowed to roll and tilt freely in its gimbals, to test and adjust the guidance and control system. Over the next five months, there were no serious mishaps, but the squibs continued to be a source of concern.

Charlie's team was looking forward to flying their rocket. It would be the largest American rocket yet built, although still only a sixth the weight of the German V-2. The first test missile was 31 feet 7 inches long, 30 inches in diameter and weighed 1307 pounds empty and 4222 pounds fully fueled. They packaged it up at Point Loma and the Marine Corps trucked it to the White Sands Proving Grounds in New Mexico, where it arrived on June 2, 1948.

White Sands was an Army test range, 140 x 54 miles, located between Las Cruces and Alamogordo. The first atomic bomb was detonated at the northern end of the range in 1945, and later that year a missile test facility was constructed in the southern end. Launch complex LC-33 was a twenty-acre fenced-in site with an L-shaped concrete pavement and multiple launching pads. The test missile would use the special pad built for V-2s, with a hole for the exhaust and a 40-foot deep flame pit below. Five

[250] MX-774 Ground to Ground Missile, CVAC Report 1496-14, December, 1947.

hundred feet to the south was the massive blockhouse, with 10-foot-thick concrete walls, topped with a solid pyramid 27 feet high. It was designed to withstand a direct hit by a V-2.[251] The designated impact area was 40 miles north of the launch pad, in a large field of white sand dunes, from which the region got its name.

For the second time, Charlie found himself close to where Robert Goddard had once worked on rocket experiments. After Goddard built the first liquid-fuel rockets in Massachusetts, he moved to Roswell, New Mexico. His privately funded test site on Salt Creek was about a hundred miles northeast of White Sands. He was the most famous rocket builder in the world, but his work was cloaked in secrecy. The German government assigned spies to gather information about his work and the type of fuel he was using, and how he cooled his engines.[252]

The test rocket flight plan called for a five-minute "warm-up" before launch, to spin up the gyros. After take-off, the engine would burn for 77 seconds, starting out in a vertical direction. Forty-six seconds into the flight, an onboard timer would pitch the rocket 7 degrees to the north. At the end of powered flight, it would be traveling at over 3400 miles per hour (Mach 5) and coast upward to 100 miles. At 210 seconds after launch, near the top of its trajectory, a Primacord charge would explosively separate the nose cone and release the parachute. In an emergency, three radio commands could be transmitted, to shut off its engine, release the nose-cone and parachute, or detonate a self-destruct charge.[253]

During the Lark missile project, one of Charlie's engineers, Travis Maloy, had experimented with a photographic telemetry recorder.[254] On the RTV-A-2 test rocket they used a similar scheme. The nose section contained a bank of dials and indicator lights with a movie camera recording tank pressures, combustion chamber pressures, skin temperatures at different points, a barometer, a stop watch, and other parameters. In addition, a radio telemetry system would transmit measurements about the guidance and propulsion system.

On July 14, 1948, after two years of design, construction and testing, the rocket was ready to be launched. Surrounded by a 60-foot gantry, it was monitored and filled with fuel. At noon, the alcohol was pumped into the fuel tanks. At 5 pm, the volatile liquid oxygen was loaded. Weather delayed the launch, and enough liquid oxygen boiled off that it had to be refilled at 6 pm. Finally the motorized gantry rolled away on its tracks.

[251] Kennedy, Gregory P., *White Sands Proving Grounds*, Schiffer Military History, 2009.
[252] Farago, Ladislas, *The Game of the Foxes*, McKay, 1971.
[253] Maloy, T.L., *Configuration for the First MX-774 Flight Missile*, April 5, 1948.
[254] Walker, Chuck, *Atlas: The Ultimate Weapon*, Apogee, 2005.

The blockhouse was not a good place to watch a launch, with its narrow slit of blast-proof windows. The true nerve center of launch operations was Tracking Station C, three miles south of the pad. Once the rocket was launched, tracking and telemetry would be monitored there. That was where Charlie joined Herbert Karsh, who was the flight control director and range safety officer. The plotting room was Karsh's operations center, where he was surrounded by telemetry chart recorders and radio operators. On the north wall, a row of large windows faced the launch complex and provided a clear view of rocket test flights.

On the roof and the grounds surrounding Station C were batteries of radar and tracking telescopes.[255] The launch would be watched and filmed through the giant lenses of Askania cine theodolites (tracking telescopes with movie cameras), Mitchell cameras, and Bowen-Knapp cameras. The range also included SCR-584 radars, the same type used to track planes and V-1 missiles during the war. Station C was in constant contact with other observation stations around the range, and Karsh had a direct phone line to the blockhouse.

Jim Crooks' prototype Doppler velocity ground station would monitor the rocket from a mile to the south of the pad, and Convair's radio telemetry receivers were set up a mile to the west. They had hoped to include the range and azimuth angle systems on the second test rocket and do full azimuth/elevation tracking on the third test; but after funding was cancelled, the Doppler speedometer was the only test of their radio guidance systems on the test missile.

If the missile went off course, Karsh could press the self-destruct button. An explosive charge of TNT was planted at the bulkhead between the fuel and oxygen tanks, sure to trigger a massive explosion and burn up the propellant so it would not fall to earth like a bomb. He was especially mindful of the dangers of firing powerful rockets, even this far out in the wilderness. A year earlier, a V-2 had gone off course and landed on the outskirts of Alamogordo. Even more embarrassing was a Hermes missile that crashed in Mexico, leaving a 50-foot crater in a cemetery outside of Juarez. Its guidance system had been installed backwards, causing it to pitch south instead of north. After that, range safety protocols were made more rigorous.

At 6:04 pm, the test conductor in the blockhouse pressed the firing button, and a few seconds later the rocket lifted off.[256] As the missile ascended in a steady vertical course without hunting, Charlie was gratified

---

[255] Rosen, Milton W., *The Viking Rocket Story*, Harper, 1955.
[256] Chapman, John L., *Atlas: The Story of a Missile*, Harper, New York, 1960.

to see the control system working perfectly. But only 12.6 seconds after lift-off, the engines shut down.[257] He was dismayed to see the exhaust flames flare and then go out, long before they should have. The rocket coasted upward, reaching 6228 feet before coming to a stop and beginning a nose dive back to earth.

At the blockhouse, some of the men had stepped outside to watch the launch. The engine shutdown had occurred before the pitch-over maneuver sent it northward, so the rocket went straight up and came straight down. Suddenly, they heard Karsh's voice shout from the loud speaker, "Burnout! She's falling…heading straight for the blockhouse!" The men scrambled back inside and closed the heavy blast doors. Only 47.5 seconds after takeoff, they felt the muffled thud of a nearby explosion.

When Charlie reached the launch site, he found a 30 foot crater with the burning fragments of the rocket that his team had spent a year preparing. Someone had attempted to send the command triggering the parachute, but due to an operator error the chute failed to deploy. With more than a ton of fuel and liquid oxygen left in its tanks, the rocket hit the ground and detonated violently. The RTV-A-2 had the dubious honor of being the only rocket at White Sands to nearly bomb the blockhouse, landing inside the fenced enclosure only 415 feet from the launch pad. Miraculously, they were able to recover and piece together some film from the smashed telemetry camera. There were indications that the liquid oxygen valve had closed, snuffing out the engine, but no clear explanation of why that had happened. One possibility was a power failure. But the engines had run normally in static tests, so why did it shut down during flight?

Back at Convair, the team studied the telemetry of the launch, trying to work out what had gone wrong. The missile's electrical system had been patched several times during static testing. At a social gathering at Irvine's home in La Jolla, some of the men decided to watch the 16 mm launch movies. They told their families the films were top secret and they were not cleared to see them, but Charlie's boys Newell and Jan sneaked in after the lights were turned out and watched from the back of the room.

One success was the guidance system. With the swiveling engines and the damped-gyro control system, the rocket deviated less than 11 feet from the vertical at 2358 feet altitude, where the engine had stopped.

The second test missile underwent a week of static tests at Point Loma and then was loaded for transport to White Sands on September 8. On September 27, the Convair team was once again preparing for a launch. The

[257] *MX-774 Ground to Ground Missile*, CVAC Report 1496-18, July & August, 1948.

rocket took off at 2:05 pm, this time reaching 54,000 feet before, once again, the engines shut down prematurely at 48 seconds. Traveling at 2500 feet/sec, momentum carried it upward for another 68 seconds. Its final altitude was never certain; one set of instruments measured 23 miles, one of the telescopes measured 33 miles.[258]

At 98 seconds, the battery failed. By 203 seconds after launch, the rocket was falling nose down at twice the speed of sound. Without electric power, the command sent to release the parachute had no effect, nor could they trigger self-destruction. Air friction was heating its skin, and the liquid oxygen boiled and burst the bulkhead between the LOX and alcohol tanks, detonating the self-destruct charge. The two mangled halves of the air frame fell more slowly then, tumbling to earth. As a result, the telemetry camera was saved from destruction, and it landed 2.5 miles from the pad. A newly added indicator light proved that the LOX valve had indeed been closed, causing the early burnout. They guessed that the pneumatic valve control system lost pressure.[259]

The Air Force had funded three test rockets, and on December 2, they prepared for one last launch. Convair had originally planned to build ten test missiles with a variety of payloads and propellant mass. The longest with the smallest payload was designed to reach an altitude of 200 miles. Test missile No. 3 had a longer payload section, giving a total length of 34 feet 8 inches. The extra payload was an improved radar transponder that worked with the SCR-584 tracking radar.[260]

At 3:01 pm, the rocket took off. It got further than the others, but the engine still shut down early, at 51.6 seconds at an altitude of 56,214 feet. It had just executed its 7° pitch, but it never had a chance to complete the maneuver, because the engines stopped one second later. Like the second missile, it reached supersonic speed. It coasted up to about 30 miles before beginning its descent. This time, a parachute release command was sent, but entanglement with an ejected piece of metal did not allow it to deploy until 45 seconds later. Knifing through the air at a thousand miles an hour, the shock of opening the chute ripped it free, and the rocket fell and exploded. The aluminum camera canister was attached to the parachute, but when they found the chute, the camera had come loose and fallen somewhere else in the desert.

---

[258] In a vacuum, the rocket should have coasted for 78 seconds, reaching 27 miles, by my calculations. The summary report in 1949 simply states that it reached 24 miles.

[259] MX-774 Ground-to-Ground Missile, CVAC Report 19, September, 1914.

[260] APN-55 radar beacon. (Maloy, T.L., *Configuration for the Third MX-774 Flight Missile*, October 21, 1948).

Finding a fallen missile was hard enough, but searching the sand dunes for a small camera seemed impossible. The base commander refused to even try. Charlie's team returned to San Diego and analyzed the flight telemetry and aerodynamics. The chief of flight test, Harold Cheney, oversaw an effort to calculate where the camera might have landed, and they came up with a one-square-mile area. The commander at White Sands agreed to send out a search party, but the camera was not found. Just as they were about to give up, one of the team realized there was a surveying mistake and they had misdirected the Army by half a mile. They searched a second time, and found it.[261]

Even after a free fall of 121,000 feet and spending eleven days in the desert, the film was still viable. Again, Charlie saw that the LOX valve had closed. After conducting some vibration tests in the lab, they finally believed they had identified the probable cause.

The test rocket had two 3000-psi nitrogen tanks. One, near the top, provided pressurization of the fuel and oxygen tanks. A small auxiliary nitrogen tank in the engine compartment pressurized the hydrogen peroxide tank and also provided pressure for pneumatic valves. The intense vibration of flight had caused the pressure regulator to resonate and leak. When the auxiliary nitrogen pressure was gone, the LOX valve had closed.[262] This explained why static tests had not revealed the problem, because there was much less vibration when the rocket was held in place. The rest of the rocket's systems appeared to be functioning, but there was no funding to build a fourth rocket, even though they were sure they knew how to fix the problem.

With the test-rocket program finished, the MX-774 program was concluded. The team members returned to other aircraft projects at Convair. But theoretical work on the intercontinental-range rocket continued, as the company gambled that the project would eventually be revived.

With a heavy warhead and no exotic super fuels, Charlie knew that the ICBM needed to be an enormous rocket with an almost impossibly light structure. But weight could only be reduced so much, or the missile would become too fragile.

To reduce weight even more, they needed to employ strategies for dropping spent sections of the rocket structure during flight. A well-known way of doing this was a two-stage rocket, but they were concerned about

---

[261] Chapman, John L., *Atlas: The Story of a Missile*, Harper, New York, 1960.
[262] "Interview of Mr. K.J. Bossart by John L. Sloop," NASA, 1974.

the unreliability they had experienced with engine ignition. What if the rocket took off successfully, but in mid-flight the second-stage engine failed to start? Furthermore, the second stage needed to ignite at extremely high altitude, where the rarefied atmosphere made the problem more difficult and unfamiliar.[263]

For a while, the team considered parallel stages, a central sustainer stage and booster stages clustered around the side. In these schemes, all the stages would ignite on the launch pad, and the boosters would be dropped when they used up their fuel. The sustainer would continue burning until the boost phase was complete. This was more reliable, because if an engine failed to start, they could all be shut down and the launch could be tried again. But they worried about the aerodynamic drag of a rocket cluster, and there was the danger that ejected empty boosters might get stuck or knock the sustainer stage off course.

Next, they developed the novel idea of annular stages, a single sleeve-like booster stage that wrapped around the sustainer, like a cartridge around a bullet. This had some aerodynamic advantages, because the rocket began with a streamlined shape similar to a single-stage rocket. It also proved to have weight advantages, with less tank surface area than a cluster of separate boosters surrounding the sustainer. Before the MX-774 contract was cancelled, they had hoped to build a two-stage 1300-mile test rocket using the annular scheme, powered by a cluster of 10,000-pound LOX/Alcohol engines that Reaction Motors Inc. was developing.

Finally, Lloyd Standley suggested an alternative scheme, which they called "one-and-a-half stages." Sustainer and booster engines would fire at launch, but they would share one propellant tank. At some point during the flight, the booster engines would be dropped, and the tank and sustainer engine would continue to accelerate. The scheme had the disadvantage that it could not discard the weight of empty tanks, but Charlie was confident he could make the common tank extremely light. It had some weight advantages over sequential staging: the sustainer engine contributed to the thrust from the start, the first-stage boosters did not have to be made big enough to carry a second stage as an inert payload.

By November 1948, Charlie's team had designed the first rockets using the one-and-a-half-stage design. The Air Force had expressed interest in a 1000-mile-range nuclear missile, carrying a 6000-pound payload. The largest engine immediately available in 1948 was the 20,000 lbs. thrust XLR-10, built by Reaction Motors Inc. for the Navy's Viking rocket. One would be used as the sustainer engine, surrounded by four more acting as boosters,

---

[263] MX-774 Ground-to-Ground Missile, Summary Report, Convair, December 1, 1949.

jettisoned during flight. Four hinge-mounted 8000-C4 engines mounted around the sustainer engine would steer the missile using the already developed RTV-A-2 control system.

Even more powerful engines were under development in 1948. At the end of the war, North American Aviation was asked by the government to study the engine technology of the V-2 and improve on its many shortcomings. To do this, they created a new division named Rocketdyne.

At 56,000 pounds of thrust, the V-2 engine was an order of magnitude more powerful than anything made before, but it had many problems. It was a complicated plumbing nightmare, with fuel separately piped to 18 small combustion sub-chambers that each fired into a main chamber. The result was heavy, poorly cooled and inefficient.

One of the problems that was limiting the size of rocket engines was combustion instability. Resonant vibration could start in the chamber, like a giant whistle driven with tremendous power. This was called "screeching," and it could destroy an engine. Purely by luck, the V-2 engine was stable, but when German researchers tried to simplify its design, their experimental engines failed catastrophically. Engineers at General Electric were the first to understand the problem, and Rocketdyne soon mastered it as well.

When Charlie talked with Rocketdyne in 1948, they were developing a 75,000-pound thrust engine for the Navaho cruise missile. The 75K engine still used the inefficient German cooling scheme and had to burn dilute alcohol. But it was simpler and more powerful than the V-2 engine.[264]

Making engines bigger did not entirely solve the long-range rocket problem. A more fundamental issue was the low exhaust velocity of engines burning alcohol. Charlie did a design study of the largest rocket he thought they could build, using five 75K engines in a one-and-a-half-stage configuration (one sustainer and four droppable boosters). It could only carry a nuclear warhead an estimated 2113 miles. To achieve a 5000 mile range, using alcohol as fuel, would require what seemed an impossibly large rocket weighing a million pounds.

If they could use liquid hydrogen (abbreviated "LH2", meaning liquid H_2), it was a different story. Charlie designed two rockets that could reach 5000 miles: a 120,000-pound missile of the annular two-stage design, and a 75,000 pound one-and-a-half-stage missile.[265] One interesting idea in Charlie's design was to surround the hydrogen tank with a layer of liquid

[264] Kraemer, Robert S., *Rocketdyne: Powering Humans Into Space*, AIAA, 2006.
[265] *Proposed Development Program on Rocket Type Missiles*, CVAC ZP-48-35003, Nov. 1948.; MX-774 Ground-to-Ground Missile, Summary Report, Convair, December 1, 1949.

oxygen, to make the thermal insulation problem somewhat easier. In the late 1940s, Aerojet Corporation was experimenting with LOX/LH2 engines, but their design for a 30,000-pound engine never materialized. The technology to burn such a high-energy fuel without destroying the engine did not yet exist.

Oxygen and hydrogen burned with such high temperature they were used to weld steel. To prevent the engine from melting, Aerojet planned to cool it by transpiration, forcing water through porous metal on the inside surface of the combustion chamber.

Aerojet was also experimenting with diborane (B_2H_6), an exotic fuel that burned with a green flame and produced even more energy than hydrogen. The Convair team produced some designs based on that propellant, but again the engine technology failed to appear. Despite the great advantage of higher exhaust speed, chemicals such as fluorine and boron compounds have never achieved widespread success due to their toxicity and instability.

In the Soviet Union, Sergei Korolev made the similar early designs based around super fuels, hoping to build a small inexpensive ICBM. His team came to the same realization as the Americans about the impracticality of that approach. Engines would get better, but it was up to the structural designers to increase the mass ratio of rockets if intercontinental range was to be achieved.

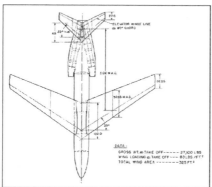

Concept art for MX-774 cruise missile and ballistic missile. Plan for MX-774A cruise missile. Hypergrid prototype on C-46 transport (*Courtesy of Bossart Family*).

American anti-aircraft battery in 1944: A. power generator, B. SCR-584 automatic tracking radar, C. M-9 analog gun computer, D. M-9 tracker, E. battery of four servo-controlled 90 mm guns. (*U.S. Army*).

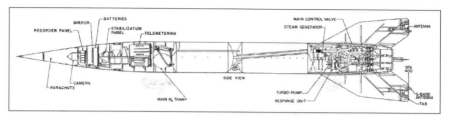

Diagram of RTV-A-2 test rocket, filling
the liquid oxygen tank, gyro guidance
system for RTV-A-2 (*Curtesy of Bossart
Family*).

The RTV-A-2 at White Sands Test Range.
test missile in flight, telemetry dials and
camera in missile nose cone (*National
Archives and Records Administration*).

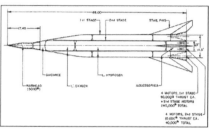

Drawing of static testing of original hydrogen-fluorine ICBM next to the RTV-A-2 test stand, laboratory setup to investigate tri-atomic hydrogen, annular two-stage ICBM powered by hydrogen, 1000-mile-range missile designed in 1948 with 1.5 stages (*Courtesy of Bossart Family*).

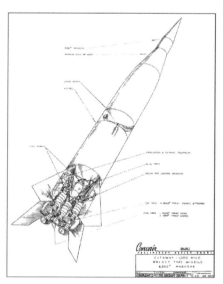

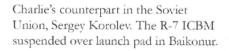

Charlie's counterpart in the Soviet Union, Sergey Korolev. The R-7 ICBM suspended over launch pad in Baikonur.

5

Charlie Atlas

The years of cancelled funding for the ICBM (1947-1951) were a "dark ages" for the Convair rocket team, as Charlie later described it.[266] He and Bill Patterson found only low-level officers in the Air Force who were enthusiastic about the "Buck Rogers" idea of a long-range rocket weapon. Generals asked them why they thought they were smarter than Vannevar Bush, the powerful scientist who had denounced long-range rockets. Their response was, "Because we studied the problem and he didn't." Even when they were testing the RTV-A-2, the Air Force had shown only lukewarm interest, sending minor personnel to observe.

Back at Convair, Charlie returned to his official duties in 1949, as chief structures engineer for the San Diego division. When he was not involved in ICBM research, he was working on the structural analysis of the Convair 340 airliner and the R3Y turboprop seaplane.[267]

This was the period of time when the war-time alliance with the Soviet Union disintegrated and the cold war began. The West was turning against communism as a series of events occurred: the overthrow of the Czech Third Republic in 1946, the Berlin Blockade from 1948-1949, the Chinese revolution in 1949, and the outbreak of the Korean War in 1950.

America's monopoly on nuclear weapons ended on August 29, 1949, when the Soviet Union detonated a 22-kiloton atomic bomb. Designated RDS-1, it was based on detailed plans of the American "Fat Man" bomb smuggled out of Los Alamos by communist sympathizers.[268] Nevertheless,

---

[266] Bossart, K.J., Letter to Edmund Beard, November, 1971.

[267] Bossart, K.J., "Design Problems of Large Rockets," *High Altitude and Satellite Rockets, Cranfield Symposium*, July 18-20, 1957. (biography on page 132).

the Russian bomb demonstrated that the Soviets were not technologically backwards, and their bomb test came much sooner than many Western experts had predicted.

By the early 1950s, the West began to realize there was a developing threat from Soviet missile technology. Even then, western intelligence analysts knew very little about the Soviet Union's rocket program. Charlie's Russian counterpart, Sergei Korolev, was an unknown in the West; his very name was a closely guarded secret not revealed until the 1960s.

On May 13, 1946, Stalin signed a state decree entitled "The Problems of Rocket Armaments."[269] With it, the resources of the Soviet state were committed to research and development of atomic-age defensive and offensive missiles. Just as Charlie had predicted, they started an effort to develop anti-aircraft rockets to shoot down American bombers and cruise missiles. Korolev was chief designer of the long-range rocket program, with the goal of developing missiles that could deliver atomic warheads to Western Europe and eventually an ICBM. Stalin saw that his country was surrounded by hostile military bases, and he believed the only true deterrence to attack would be the ability to strike at the American mainland.

At the Soviet missile test range in Kapustin Yar, Korolev's team launched the first captured V-2 in 1947. In October of 1948, he tested the R-1, a copy of the V-2 built from scratch, entirely with Russian materials. Their goal was not simply to duplicate the V-2, but to understand and develop a complete industrial infrastructure for manufacturing rockets. Once the R-1 was complete, most of their captured German scientists were deported, providing little useful information to the CIA about subsequent development of missile technology. Two years after the R-1, the Soviets completed the R-2 with twice the range. By the time von Braun's 250-mile Redstone was ready in 1953, the Russians had the 750-mile R-5, which was adapted to carry an atomic warhead.

The Soviet ICBM program began officially with "Theme N-3" in December, 1950. It included the 3000-km-range R-3 missile, and a design study for a rocket with a range of 10,000 km (6200 miles). Late in 1951, an intelligence report claimed the Soviet Union was developing an engine with 265,000 pounds of thrust, twice the power of Rocketdyne's latest engine.[270] This may have been the RD-110 engine, developed for the R-3. The massive engine was based on a German design concept that proved to be

---

[268] Medved, Aleksandr Nikolaevich, "K Istorii Sozdaniya Pervoi Otechestvennoi Yadernoi Bomby" (History of the Creation of the First Domestic Nuclear Bomb), *Dvigatel*, No. 3, 2009.

[269] "*Voprosy Reaktivnogo Voorzheniya*"

[270] Neufeld, Jacob, *The Development of Ballistic Missiles in the United States Air Force, 1945-1960*, Office of Air Force History, Washington, 1990.

unsound. Korolev was hoping to build a 7000-km-range missile from three R-3s arranged in a parallel-stage configuration. If it had succeeded in the mid-1950s, it would have been a devastating strategic advantage.

However, the R-3 never materialized, in part because its massive engine proved to be unstable. The Soviet ICBM in its final successful form was specified in February of 1953 in a program called "Theme T-1."[271] It would be a parallel-stage missile with a range of 8000 km (5000 miles), a payload of 3 tons, and an accuracy of 15 km (9 miles). Economically and technologically, the Soviet Union lagged behind America, but like the tale of the tortoise and the hare, they made slow and steady progress while America vacillated about building long-range rockets.

In the United States, technological developments were changing the military's opinion about ICBMs. When Convair's MX-774 project was cancelled, the Air Force's RAND think tank was tasked with monitoring the issue of long-range missiles. In December of 1950, RAND reported that improvements in rocket-engine technology and advances in guidance-system accuracy made the ICBM more feasible. In January that year, President Truman authorized the development of the hydrogen "super bomb." A thousand times more powerful than the atomic bomb, a hydrogen warhead made the ICBM even more compelling, and its larger blast radius relaxed the requirements for guidance accuracy.

Since the cancellation of the ICBM project, at least one influential official supported the idea of an intercontinental missile: General Donald Putt, a former student of von Kármán's.[272] Putt was soon to be head of the new Air Research and Development Command (ARDC). In 1950, at a Christmas party in Washington D.C., a Convair representative told General Putt that the board of directors was on the verge of giving up on Charlie's long-range missile research. Putt was concerned, and responded, "I have just found half a million dollars in the bottom of the drawer."[273]

On January 23, 1951, the Air Force officially awarded Convair the $500,000 ICBM study contract that Putt had promised. The willingness to resume funding of ICBM research reflected the increasing military budget. MX-774 had been cancelled in the drastic spending cuts after the Second

[271] Keldysh, M.V., *Tvorcheskoi Nasledie Akademika Sergeya Pavlovicha Koroleva*, Nauka, Moscow, 1980.; Raushenbakh, B.V. (ed), *S.P. Korolev, i Ego Delo*, Nauka, Moscow 1998.; Siddiqi, Asif A., *The Red Rocket's Glare*, Cambridge University Press, 2010. Like the U.S., the Soviets also began development of intercontinental cruise missiles, under Theme-T2.
[272] Neufeld, Jacob, *The Development of Ballistic Missiles in the United States Air Force, 1945-1960*, Office of Air Force History, Washington, 1990.
[273] Pearson, Drew, "Big Businessmen Deserve Credit for Mercury Orbit," *Washington Merry-Go-Round*, Mar 9, 1962.

World War, but with the Korean War beginning in 1950, the military budget doubled in 1951 and doubled again the next year.

Convair asked Charlie to be the project engineer and assemble his rocket team again. They wanted a good code name for the project, before the Air Force selected one. The team discussed it, and someone suggested "Box Car." Someone else suggested "Hot Rod." Charlie suggested "Atlas," from Greek mythology, the titan who held up the sky. As he later explained, there were two reasons for selecting it: "I finally came up with that name because it gave a feeling of worldwide significance, and I felt the name would get the support of our parent company as that time—Floyd Odlum's Atlas Corporation." The Air Force liked it too, and MX-1593 officially became Project Atlas.[274]

The specifications for the missile were daunting. It must deliver an 8000 pound warhead to a distance of 5000 nautical miles and strike the target with an accuracy of 1500 feet. This extreme accuracy reflected the half-mile kill radius of a 32-kiloton atomic bomb (the high-efficiency W-13 warhead). Fifteen hundred feet was the standard accuracy for high altitude manned strategic bombers, from 25,000 feet, using the Norden bombsight. The range was later increased to 5500 nautical miles, which was one quarter of the circumference of the earth.

The Air Force asked Convair to evaluate and compare two reentry schemes: a ballistic nose cone that enters at supersonic speed and a gliding warhead that coasts toward its target on wings after reentry. The latter was an idea championed by the Germans, who had planned a transatlantic missile of the boost-glide type. Their A-9/A-10 would have consisted of a V-2 rocket with wings boosted by a larger first stage with a cluster of engines. But von Braun's war-time tests failed when the wings broke off at supersonic speed (not an impressive example of stress analysis). Charlie's team had already studied boost-glide missiles in 1949,[275] and in an eight-volume July 1951 report, they recommended that the Air Force abandon the boost-glide approach. As a rocket, it presented all the technical challenges of the ballistic missile, and approaching the target as a gliding subsonic aircraft, it had all the vulnerabilities of a cruise missile.

In 1951, Rocketdyne had a more powerful engine, the 120K. They abandoned the German cooling scheme and used an entirely new method, with incoming fuel flowing through copper tubes that lined the inside surface of the combustion chamber.[276] Like the 75K, it burned alcohol, but

[274] Stone, Frank, "Charlie Bossart: Stroller Gazes at the Sky," *San Diego Evening Tribune*, March 12, 1960.

[275] Bossart, K.J., "Notes on Long Range Missile Design," Report ZP-48-35004, January, 1949.

[276] Winter, Frank H. *On the Spaghetti Trail*, 54th IAF Congress, 2003.

at 92.5% concentration and higher chamber pressure, producing 120,000 pounds of thrust and about 5 percent higher exhaust speed. In another year, they would boost the thrust and exhaust speed even more, by burning kerosene.[277] With that, the legacy of the V-2 engine was entirely replaced by modern engine technology, more or less identical to the engines of today.

By September of 1951, Charlie's team was ready to present their design for an ICBM, at a meeting with Air Force officials at the Lord Baltimore Hotel in Maryland. It was a colossal rocket, 160 feet tall and 12 feet in diameter, weighing 670,000 pounds. The one-and-a-half-stage design used seven of the 120K engines to produce 840,000 pounds of take-off thrust. Five of the engines were boosters that would be jettisoned with the tail section, and two were sustainer engines that remained with the rocket until engine shut-down. In addition to the seven large engines, two of the RMI 20K engines were included for steering.

The first Atlas design was more than twenty times the mass of the V-2, but as Charlie argued, large size did not necessarily make a rocket more difficult to develop and operate. He proved that the structural strength needed to deal with internal pressure and stresses on the rocket scaled with size. The stress caused by aerodynamic drag actually became proportionally smaller as rocket size increased.[278] Flight control became more stable for larger rockets, as he said to his team, "It's like a mouse and an elephant. The mouse can make sharp turns. The elephant is sluggish and has a lot more time to apply corrections."

The New Year began with sad news from Belgium. In January 1952, Charlie learned that his mother was undergoing cancer surgery, and in March he received a telegram reporting her death. For the second time in two years he had to make an unhappy flight back to Antwerp for a funeral. With both their children living in other countries, Louis and Carolina had been cared for by Aunt Vire and her daughter Daisy. In appreciation of all their kindness and support, Charlie and Dora decided to give the Bossart Kalmthout home to Daisy.

Two months after his return from Belgium, Charlie got an unexpected visit from Wernher von Braun. This may have been the first time the two great rocket designers met, but they knew each other by reputation. Von

---

[277] Commonly, engines of this type are said to use LOX/kerosene. More accurately, rocket fuel was derived from jet fuel, which was a wide-cut petroleum distillate containing everything from gasoline to kerosene. This was further purified further for rocketry to remove substances that would carbonize or polymerize while passing through the cooling tubes inside the engine.
[278] Bossart, K.J., "Design Problems of Large Rockets," *High Altitude and Satellite Rockets, Cranfield Symposium*, July 18-20, 1957.

Braun was engaged in a national campaign to raise interest in space travel, writing a series of articles in Collier's Magazine and giving lectures. During the war, he and some of the V-2 engineers had formulated ideas about space stations and missions to the Moon and Mars. Now, he was putting together a committee to study and advocate launching an artificial satellite. In a letter to a colleague, von Braun listed the ten engineers and scientists he had invited, but he elaborated on his meeting with Charlie, who shared his passion for rockets. They discussed how difficult it was to find people of imagination and experience. Von Braun wrote:

> *There is a very acute shortage of people with these qualifications in the guided missile and supersonic aircraft programs. I discussed this question with Mr. Bossart of Convair and found him in full accord with my own opinion: Both of us believe that a satellite program has such a tremendous appeal to thousands of scientists and engineers that it would actually constitute a very powerful magnet to attract people from other fields of engineering* [279]

Interest in space travel had motivated the original research on long-range rockets, long before the idea of ballistic missiles. In the mid-19th century, Jules Verne wrote about a trip to the Moon, and his science fiction novels inspired many young people to study science. Tsiolkovsky was the first to apply scientific rigor to the problem, even though his interest in space travel was motivated by religious mysticism. Goddard wrote remarkable speculations about space travel to his sponsors, proposing to send unmanned space probes with cameras to the Moon and Mars. By the 1920s, the first public space-exploration society was started in the Soviet Union, and a few years later, several rocket research clubs appeared in Germany, including the one to which von Braun belonged. The American Rocket Society was formed in 1930, and the British Interplanetary Society began in 1933.

After the Second World War, von Braun presented the Americans with a report detailing German ideas about space travel, and initially there was a flurry of enthusiasm in the Navy and Air Force. The Navy requested proposals for a High Altitude Test Vehicle (HATV), which was to be a single stage LOX/LH2 rocket designed to enter orbit. Not to be outdone, the Air Force commissioned RAND to design a multi-stage "World-Circling Spaceship." But post-war budget cuts rapidly extinguished these somewhat unrealistic projects.

---

[279] Letter from von Braun to Dr. A.V. Grosse, June 21, 1952.

Even before von Braun's visit, Charlie had thought about space travel and was well informed on the subject. In January of 1952, he was interviewed by a local magazine in San Diego and asked about trips to the Moon.[280] He predicted that an unmanned rocket could hit the Moon by 1962, and a manned landing could be performed by 1972. He mentioned that a trip to Mars would take eight months, which is the duration of a Hohmann transfer orbit from Earth to Mars, and he talked about the possibility of putting a guided missile into orbit to create a satellite.

However, it was the military application of rocketry that attracted the necessary financial support to build large rockets, beginning with the V-2 in Germany and eventually the ICBM with its nuclear warhead. In fact, the design and feasibility of the Atlas was closely linked to the evolution of nuclear weapons. As the bombs became more powerful, the accuracy of the ICBM could be relaxed. As bombs became smaller and lighter, the rocket could be reduced in size and cost.

On November 1, 1952, the U.S.A. detonated the world's first hydrogen bomb, in an operation code named Ivy Mike. The explosion evaporated an entire island in the Pacific, leaving a crater in the ocean floor more than a mile across. With a yield of 10 megatons, it was 500 times the power of the first A-bomb. It produced radiation so intense that new chemical elements were created and discovered in the fallout.[281] But Ivy Mike was an experiment and far from being a deliverable weapon. Based on liquid heavy hydrogen (deuterium), it was a so-called "wet" bomb, consisting of a cylinder twenty feet tall and weighing more than 80 tons.

Even before the Ivy Mike test, scientists at Los Alamos were at work designing the W-15 thermonuclear warhead, projected to yield 1.7 megatons. At 6400 pounds, it was just as heavy as the A-bomb that Atlas was designed to carry. The W-15 was not exactly a true hydrogen bomb. It used hydrogen fusion to boost the fission explosion of a large mass of uranium. Los Alamos promised lighter warheads of equal power, as more energy was derived from the fusion of lightweight hydrogen and less from the fission of heavy uranium. The next generation W-29 warhead was predicted to weigh half as much. Charlie's team was not privy to these details at the time, but the Air Force revised its requirements for the missile as these advances in weapons technology unfolded.

In December, the Air Force's Scientific Advisory Board was asked to evaluate the ICBM problem. The board was chaired by von Kármán's

---

[280] "Guided Missiles: Death from the Sky!", POINT, San Diego Newsweekly, February 1, 1952.
[281] Einsteinium and Fermium, elements 99 and 100 respectively.

successor, Dr. Clark Millikan,[282] a professor at Caltech who headed the Jet Propulsion Laboratory. The committee updated the specifications for the missile to more sensible values—the warhead weight specification was reduced to 3000 pounds (the predicted weight of the W-29), and an accuracy of 1 mile was recommended.

The report was positive about Convair's work, but to their disappointment, it advocated a slow conservative development plan that would cover ten years, not the crash program that Charlie and his management thought was necessary.[283] Millikan's committee recommended that Convair first build two test missiles. The X-11 would be an 80,000 pound rocket, 95 feet long and 12 feet in diameter, with a single 120K engine burning LOX and alcohol. It was designed to reach an altitude of 330 miles and could help test reentry systems. Next would come the X-12, which would have two booster engines in addition to the sustainer engine. It was designed to test the one-and-a-half-stage concept and an ejected nose cone, reaching a range of 1400 nautical miles. Neither the X-11 nor X-12 was ever built.

In response to the lighter warhead specification, Charlie's team redesigned the Atlas. The new rocket was 110 feet long, weighing 440,100 pounds at launch.[284] The number of engines was reduced to five, a single sustainer engine with 123,300 pounds of thrust, gimbaled for steering the missile, and four booster engines of 133,200 pounds, which would be jettisoned after two minutes of flight. Convair had asked Rocketdyne to modify their engines to burn hydrocarbon jet fuel, which produced greater thrust and a 10 percent increase in exhaust velocity.[285]

In operation, the missile would lift off under the control of gyroscopic guidance. At 60,000 feet, it would come into radio contact with the Azusa guidance station, which was 200 miles down range. Initially, it would only be tracked by Azusa, but still controlled by the rocket's gyros. At 200,000 feet, the booster engines would be dropped, and Azusa would begin transmitting commands for high-accuracy radio guidance. At about five minutes, the engines would cut off, when Azusa's computers determined the rocket had reached the correct speed. A few seconds later, the warhead would be ejected, and the ballistic phase of the flight would begin. Atmospheric reentry would occur 30 minutes after launch. It would be

---

[282] Clark's father was the Nobel Laureate Robert Millikan, famous for the "oil drop" experiment that measured the charge of the electron.

[283] Beard, Edmund, *Developing the ICBM*, Columbia Univ. Press, NY, 1976.

[284] *MX-1593 Pilotless Spacecraft*, Consolidated-Vultee Report, August 20, 1953.

[285] Patterson, William H., *The Evolution of a New Technology Concept in the U.S.A.*, 1985.; Sutton, George R., *History of Liquid Propellant Rocket Engines*, AAIA, 2006.

visible to ground radar for only about 15 seconds before reaching its target, traveling too fast to shoot down.

The Air Force designated the prototype missile XB-65, choosing the abbreviation for "experimental bomber." As some saw it, when the missile ejected its warhead, it was dropping a bomb (which would fall for 30 minutes before hitting the Earth).[286] From the standpoint of physics, that is a perfectly correct way of looking at it. The warhead would be in free fall, even though its momentum carries it upward for 15 minutes.

The MX-1593 specification made the atmospheric reentry problem particularly difficult. It required the warhead to approach the target at Mach 6, to evade possible defense systems. That ruled out Charlie's plan to use a blunt reentry vehicle, like the spherical warhead designed for MX-774, which slowed to about Mach 1.

Instead, they had to design an aerodynamic needle-like warhead. It would separate from the main rocket after the boost phase of four or five minutes. Internally, a gyro orientation sensor and a pair of reaction wheels kept the warhead oriented nose first. Arcing to a maximum altitude of 500 nautical miles, it would reenter the atmosphere like a lance, slowing down less than the blunt spherical design. When it got close to the target, a proximity fuze would detonate the nuclear bomb.

Unfortunately, this meant more air friction and a longer period of time exposed to the intense heating of hypersonic travel through the atmosphere. Recalling the experiments that Rocketdyne had done with transpiration cooling of combustion chambers, they decided to try the same idea to dissipate the heat of reentry. The warhead would contain a reservoir of water. During reentry, the deceleration of air resistance would force the water forward, where it would bleed through a porous magnorite tip and through the porous metal skin. The water would boil as it sweated from the surface of the warhead, creating a protective layer of steam and carrying away the heat. To test the concept, Convair built an oxygen/hydrogen flame wind tunnel able to produce a Mach 7 blast at 4500° F. However, even that was far from the extreme conditions of reentry, and specifications for the Atlas were changed before the transpiration heat shield was fully developed and proven.[287]

---

[286] Convair Film Report ZR-7-554-1, Atlas Annual Report, 1954.

[287] Heppenheimer, T.A., *Facing the Heat Barrier: A History of Hypersonics*, NASA, 2007.; *MX-774 Ground to Ground Missile: Summary Report*, CVAC Report, December, 1949; MX-1593 Pilotless Spacecraft, CVAC, August 1953; Convair Film Report ZR-7-554-1, Atlas Annual Report, 1954.

Crooks' radio guidance system controlled the missile during the five-minute boost phase, ensuring a very exact direction and speed. But after engine shut-down, the missile continued for half an hour as an unguided projectile subject to the forces of gravity. To hit the target, it was necessary to understand exactly how the warhead would travel during the free ballistic phase of its flight. That presented another research problem for Charlie.

Charlie's team had access to powerful instruments for studying the ballistic-trajectory problem. During the MX-774 project, the RTV-A-2 guidance system was simulated with Caltech's analog computer, but by the time the Atlas was under development, Convair's own resources allowed them to study the trajectory and flight dynamics of the missile from launch to impact. The Convair Analog Computer was the largest in the world at that time, custom designed by their engineers. Occupying two floors of an office building, it was assembled at a cost of $1.5 million and consisted of 67 racks of electronics, 550 operational amplifiers, and 8500 vacuum tubes. It consumed 100 kilowatts of power and operated 24 hours a day, solving structural analysis problems or controlling a cockpit flight simulator.[288]

They also had access to state-of-the-art digital computers, although this was early in the evolution of those machines. The stress analysis group that Charlie headed was particularly savvy about computers. In the 1940s, they were among the first engineers at Convair to automate tedious calculations by borrowing time on the IBM card programmed calculators in the accounting department. By 1952, the stress group had their own IBM 701 computer.[289]

Charlie hired one of the foremost experts on ballistic trajectories and orbits to consult with the Atlas team. In the summer of 1953, Prof. Paul Herget spent two months at Convair, helping them "hit Moscow from Kansas" as he later quipped.[290] An astronomer at the Cincinnati Observatory, Herget was an early pioneer in the use of computers to calculate planetary orbits. The ballistic trajectory of the Atlas was elliptical, like a satellite orbit except it happened to intersect the Earth at the launch and target points. Of course, the rotation of the Earth had to be taken into account, since the target would move hundreds of miles during the 30 minutes of flight (at the latitude of Cape Canaveral, the surface of the Earth was moving at more than 900 mph). They also discovered that it was important to correct for the slight flattening (oblateness) of the shape of the Earth, which could perturb the path of the missile by several miles. They

---

[288] Small, James S., *The Analogue Alternative*, Routledge, London, 2001.

[289] Rogers, Stanley, Interview by Smithsonian Computer History Project, Aug 9, 1973.

[290] Interview with Dr. Paul Herget, American Institute of Physics, April 20, 1977.

checked other possible forces, and their calculations showed that the gravitational pull of the Moon and planets could be safely ignored.

While working at Convair, Herget stayed at Charlie's home.[291] Connie had decided they needed a new car, so while Charlie and his guest stayed in San Diego, she and the children flew to Detroit and picked up their new seafoam-green Ford station wagon. In those days, Detroit automakers added a "destination charge" to the price of cars, depending on the distance they had to be shipped. In Southern California, it amounted to a substantial $300 ($2600 in today's dollars).

But more important than saving the money, it was a good excuse to take a vacation and visit Connie's relatives in the East. They drove across Canada, sight-seeing and stopping at the Bay of Fundy to witness the largest tidal bore in the world. After seeing Halifax and Boston, they traveled south to spend time with Connie's sisters, and then drove back across the country to San Diego.

When Connie and the children returned home, they found the two busy scientists had consumed all the food in the house, including the children's breakfast cereal. The goldfish pond that their father was supposed to take care of was overgrown, with no sign of fish. In the kitchen, Connie was greeted by the sight of every dish they owned, dirty and stacked in the sink.

1953 began with a new president in the White House, and Convair was hoping the new Eisenhower/Nixon administration would increase the priority of the ICBM program. Bill Paterson was a friend of Richard Nixon from their days in Whittier College, and he had enthusiastically campaigned for the Republican ticket.[292] Although Charlie was not very political, his sons mowed "IKE/DICK" into the grass of their front lawn, and they helped Bill with door-to-door campaigning. When Eisenhower won the election, Bill treated the boys to all the ice cream they could eat. An effort began immediately to educate the new President and Vice President about the ICBM program.

After bringing the Korean War to an end in the summer of 1953, Eisenhower planned to rely more on deterrence than military interventions. So while he reduced the military budget, the Air Force strategic bomber fleet and the ICBM program ultimately benefited from his policy.[293] The President initiated an extensive review of all military projects, and Trevor Gardner was tapped to gather information on the ballistic missile program.

---

[291] Newell Bossart, *personal communications*, 2012.
[292] Newell Bossart, *personal communications*, 2012.; Cheatham, Mike, *No Man Walks Alone: the Life and Times of Thomas G. Pownall*, Mercer University Press, 2003.;
[293] Perry, Robert L., *The Ballistic Missile Decisions*, RAND Corporation, October 1967.

Gardner would become one of the most influential supporters of the Atlas project, though not always in a manner that Convair wanted. Born in Cardiff, Wales, he became a naturalized American citizen just a year after Charlie did. During the war, Gardner was a section chief on Project Camel at Caltech, making rocket components for the Navy and the atom bomb program. A few years after the war, he started an electronics firm, and in 1953 he entered public service, joining the Eisenhower administration as the Air Force Secretary's assistant for research and development. He had a reputation as brilliant, someone who got things done, but a blunt and sometimes abrasive personality.[294]

Another central figure was Bernard Schriever, who would eventually lead the Air Force missile command. Schriever was born in Germany. His father was an engineer on a steamship passenger liner that was seized in New York Harbor during World War One. After the war, his family chose to stay in the United States and become naturalized citizens. In the early 1930s, Bernard became an Army Air Corps pilot and later earned a degree in aeronautical engineering from Stanford University. After serving in the Pacific during the Second World War, Schriever was appointed chief Air Forces scientific liaison, by General Hap Arnold. Working closely with Theodor von Kármán, Schriever made connections with both the upper echelon of the Air Force and the academic science community.[295]

In March of 1953, Schriever was attending a meeting of the Air Force Scientific Advisory Board. The country's leading physicist in the H-Bomb program, Dr. Edward Teller, made the prediction that a high-yield thermonuclear warhead would soon weigh only 1500 pounds. Schriever was shocked by this news. He knew the implications for the ICBM project, that the missile might be halved in size if the warhead could be reduced from 3000 pounds to 1500. He followed up with a visit to John von Neumann, a leading scientist at the Princeton Institute for Advanced Study; and he corroborated Teller's claim.

What Teller was referring to was the so-called "dry" bomb that physicists were developing. Instead of cumbersome apparatus containing liquid hydrogen, they wanted to use a solid compound of deuterium and the isotope lithium-6. When detonated, the intense neutron radiation in the core of the bomb would convert lithium-6 into tritium, another isotope of hydrogen that was an even better than deuterium as fuel for nuclear fusion.[296] It was an elegant idea and a highly classified secret.

---

[294] "Project Camel," *Manhattan District History*, Dept. of Energy, 1948.; *Victor V. Veysey Interviewed*, California Institute of Technology Archives, 1993.

[295] Neufeld, Jacob, "Bernard A. Schriever: Challenging the Unknown," *Flight, the 100th Anniversary*, Office of Air Force History, 2005.

In August, 1953, the Soviet Union detonated a 400-kiloton bomb at a test site in eastern Kazakhstan. It was 20 times the power of the first A-Bomb. When the fallout was analyzed, American scientists were dismayed to discover the presence of lithium-6, because it meant the Soviets were well along in developing a dry bomb. The Soviet code name for the test bomb was RDS-6s. The "s" standing for *sloyka*, a layered Russian pastry that reflected the structure, layers of uranium and lithium. It was a fusion-boosted atomic bomb, but not a true H-bomb like America's Ivy Mike blast.

America tested the first true dry bomb on March 1 of 1954. Operation Castle Bravo, in the Pacific islands, included a lithium-based bomb with a calculated yield of 3 to 5 megatons. Due to a mistake in the physics calculations, the actual yield was 15 megatons, the biggest nuclear explosion ever set off by the U.S.A. The unexpectedly powerful blast almost injured some of the closer observers. The Castle Bravo device weighed 23,500 pounds, which came to 1700 pounds per megaton. This supported Teller's claim that a megaton weapon might weigh only 1500 pounds.

Trevor Gardner was tasked with studying the ICBM problem in June of 1953, and he was well aware of the advances in nuclear weapons. On June 30, he asked Charlie, Bill Patterson and Jim Crooks to meet with him in Washington, DC. They talked for several hours about missile design concepts and the technical problems of guidance and reentry. Charlie asked for three changes to the ICBM specifications: 1) a reduction of target impact speed from Mach 6 to Mach 1 so they could use a blunt reentry vehicle; 2) relaxation of the accuracy from 1500 ft to 5000 ft; and 3) reduction of the weight of the warhead from 7000 lbs. to 3000 lbs.[297]

Gardner liked their Atlas design and agreed that the ICBM was the "ultimate means of delivering atomic bombs." He also was not happy with the plodding pace of Millikan's missile research schedule, and he asked Convair to design a plan for a crash program for Atlas. They met again a month later and presented the accelerated development plan. Charlie told Gardner that Convair could get the Atlas operational by 1958, at a total cost of $2.75 billion.[298]

Gardner soon discovered what Convair's team had already experienced, that there was conservative resistance to the ICBM concept, including

[296] Common hydrogen has an atomic nucleus consisting of just a single proton. The deuterium nucleus has a proton and a neutron. Tritium has a proton and two neutrons, and it is radioactive.
[297] Patterson, William H., *The Evolution of a New Technology Concept in the U.S.A.*, 1985.
[298] "Interview of Mr. K.J. Bossart by John L. Sloop," NASA, 1974.; Beard, Edmund, *Developing the ICBM*, Columbia Univ. Press, NY, 1976.

resistance from the new Secretary of Defense. He turned to John von Neumann at Princeton to form two prestigious committees to support the ICBM concept. In particular, he hoped to loosen the specifications of MX-1593 to make the missile more feasible: reducing the weight of the payload and relaxing the accuracy of the missile.

The first committee would study the H-bomb question and hopefully legitimize Teller's prediction of a 1500-pound warhead. The second committee would study and make recommendations about strategic missile technology. Gardner and Schriever realized that the Scientific Advisory Board no longer had the clout to change Air Force policy on this issue. Instead, they gathered a group of the most famous scientists in the country. As Gardner later said, "The aim was to create a document so hot and of such eminence that no one could pooh-pooh it."[299]

The Strategic Missiles Evaluation Committee was established at the end of October, and soon came to be called the "Teapot Committee." It included some of the top scientists in the country: John von Neuman from Princeton; Clark Millikan, Charles Lauritsen and Louis Dunn from Caltech; Hendrik Bode from Bell Telephone Laboratory; Allen Puckett from Hughes Aircraft; George Kistiakowsky from Harvard; and Jerome Wiesner and Lawrence Hyland from MIT. The recently promoted General Schriever also observed and participated in the committee.

After years of battling apathy and skepticism, Charlie and his team were about to face the opposite problem: an aggressive new opponent who saw the value of long-range missiles and would challenge Convair for control of the Atlas project or even push them out entirely. Simon Ramo and Dean Wooldridge were two engineers from Hughes Aircraft invited by Gardner to assist the committee. Just a month before the formation of Teapot, they had quit their jobs to form a company. Gardner knew Ramo from the late 1930s, when they both worked at General Electric.[300] While not as senior as the members of the committee, Ramo and Wooldridge did a lot of the leg work for them and had considerable influence.

One of the questions that the committee had to deal with was the relative merits of cruise missile versus ballistic missile. Each of the three corporations working on intercontinental missiles appeared before the committee to advocate its approach. Northrop was building the subsonic turbojet cruise missile called Snark. Under development since 1946, Snark was the favorite of the Air Force, although Gardner (like Charlie) doubted

[299] Chapman, John L., *Atlas: The Story of a Missile*, Harper, New York, 1960.
[300] Johnson, Stephen B., *The United States Air Force and the Culture of Innovation*, U.S. GPO, 2002.; Nieburg, H.L., *In the Name of Science*, Quadrangle Books, 1966.

its survival capability against Soviet anti-aircraft defenses. North American Aviation argued for their supersonic ramjet missile, Navaho. Also in development since 1946, it had evolved from a short-range boost-glide missile into an intercontinental cruise missile. Its supersonic speed made it more survivable, but still inferior to a ballistic missile.

Ironically, the Navaho project helped spawn Rocketdyne's new engines that made the Atlas possible. Although they were rivals for the missile contract, the Rocketdyne division of NAA had cooperated fully with Convair, working with them concurrently with their own Navaho project.

When it was their turn to present to the committee, Convair expounded on the virtues of their ballistic rocket. The Atlas was designed to accelerate to 16,000 mph in order to achieve its maximum range of 5500 nautical miles. It would arrive with little warning and at too great a speed to be stopped by any known anti-aircraft defense technology.

However, one of the engineers from North American Aviation claimed to have calculated that the Atlas could reach a distance of only 3000 miles. Charlie did not believe his own trajectory calculations could be so wrong, but it turned out the man from NAA had made an embarrassing mistake. Instead of using an elliptical trajectory around the Earth's center of gravity, he had used the approximation of a parabolic trajectory in a uniform gravitational field, suitable only for short-range artillery. In Charlie's words, "Our critics had figured their range on a flat earth instead of a round earth."[301]

On February 10, 1954, the Teapot Committee released their official report. The Snark and Navaho projects were continued, even though Gardner was not very enthusiastic (both projects were eventually cancelled). For Atlas, the report called for a highly accelerated development program, leading to an operational system in six or eight years. The committee relaxed the accuracy of the rocket to two or three nautical miles, and the warhead weight was specified as 1500 pounds, in agreement with von Neumann and Teller's opinions. When it was finally developed, the W-49 bomb, carried by Atlas, was 1640 pounds, with a yield of 1.44 megatons.[302]

The RAND think tank submitted a report on ICBMs just a few days before the Teapot Committee, and it substantially agreed—not surprisingly, since there was considerable cross talk, and the Teapot Committee used a lot of the data gathered by RAND.

---

[301] "Interview of Mr. K.J. Bossart by John L. Sloop," NASA, 1974.; My calculations corroborates Bossart's story: A range of 5500 nautical miles is achieved, with an initial pitch of 22°. In a flat-earth calculation, optimal launch angle is 45° and the range is only 2700 nautical miles.
[302] In 1956, Edward Teller predicted a 1 megaton warhead would ultimately be reduced to 600 lbs., and this was achieved by 1963, with the W-56 warhead for the Minuteman missile.

The lower accuracy and reduced payload were things Charlie and Bill Patterson had asked for from Trevor Gardner. But the rest of the report came as a shock to Charlie's team and Convair's executives. The Atlas section of the report began ominously: "While much credit is due Convair for pioneering work...." The committee recommended that all engineering work at Convair be halted and that the project undergo a "radical reorganization."

Traditionally, the Air Force chose a prime contractor who did design and managed subcontractors. But instead, the committee wanted to create a scientific industrial organization that would be outside the military and manage all contractors.

In the committee meetings, Ramo was critical of Convair's nose cone design in particular,[303] using it as an example of why they were not qualified to be a prime contractor. He described Convair's reentry vehicle as a futile attempt to use a heat-resistant "super ceramic," which was a misleading characterization of the research that Charlie's team had done on blunt reentry vehicles and transpiration cooling.

The Teapot Committee had also been unhappy about Convair's desire to build the five-engine missile. Ramo wanted to aggressively optimize the size of the missile, but Charlie was concerned that there would be delays and there would be no room for error in the weight of the yet-to-be-designed warhead or the anticipated thrust of next-generation engines.[304] What was the point of the crash development schedule he had prepared for Gardner, if they were going to lose a year in redesigning and reorganizing?

Franklin Collbohm, the head of RAND, agreed with Convair's viewpoint and thought the fastest route to an operational ICBM was to build the already designed rocket. He said that a number of competent companies already existed that could do the work, while Ramo-Wooldridge had "no demonstrated competence."[305] Some on the committee felt that they were simply there as a prestigious rubber stamp. As Jerome Wiesner from MIT later said, "Our decision was merely whether or not to participate rather than try to change what the Air Force was doing."

In part, the conflict was a clash between the cultures of science and engineering. No one could argue that Convair, which built the B-36, did not understand complex systems engineering. But Ramo-Wooldridge girded themselves in the authority of prestigious university professors, arguing that Atlas contained fundamental scientific research problems that were

---

[303] *The Atlas Nose Cone*, Report RW-EO-0110560b, December 12, 1956.
[304] Interview of Mr. K.J. Bossart by John L. Sloop, NASA, 1974.
[305] Nieburg, H.L., *In the Name of Science*, Quadrangle Books, 1966.

equivalent to winning five Nobel Prizes. As Ramo put it, "The plumbers at these aircraft companies aren't capable."[306]

It was an argument that resonated with some of the academics on the Teapot Committee. Others in industry and the Air Force believed the exact opposite, that it was an engineering task that would only be disrupted and delayed by the meddling of professors and committees. As Col. Edward Hall, Schriever's head of propulsion, said "The great scientists of R-W couldn't do the job, because the ballistic missile was not a science job."[307]

On February 26, the major parties gathered in Washington, DC, to discuss the consequences of the Teapot-Committee report with the Air Force top brass. But when Ramo and Schriever arrived, there was a surprise waiting. Sitting among the officers was retired Air Force General Joseph McNarney, who was now the president of Convair.[308] Charlie and Bill had given their boss a heads up before the committee's report was released, and McNarney had flown to Washington to bypass the bureaucrats and talk directly with the "blue-uniform Air Force." At the meeting, he convinced Gardner and the officers that if they were going to create a new management organization, it should be inside the Air Force and led by a general. This at least scuttled the idea of putting the Ramo-Wooldridge Corporation directly in charge of Atlas.

That summer of 1954, the Western Development Division (WDD) was created. General Schriever was appointed head and given authority over Air Force missile programs and granted special authority to cut through procurement red tape. Gardner and Schriever decided that Ramo-Wooldridge Corporation would be the systems manager of the ICBM project, and initially, Convair was stripped of all responsibility for Atlas except the airframe design. Their years of research on reentry vehicles and guidance systems were dismissed, and for the last half of 1954, Charlie and his colleagues were unsure if any of their Atlas project would be left for them.

Not surprisingly, Convair was unhappy with this arrangement, and in particular, they thought Ramo-Wooldridge was unnecessary. They did not want the extra layer of management, and they were not eager to share industrial trade secrets with a company they did not trust. Some saw it as a ploy to extract profit from a business Convair had spent years fostering. Bill

---

[306] Patterson, William H., *The Evolution of a New Technology Concept in the U.S.A.*, 1985.; Interview with Dr. Marvin Stern, American Institute of Physics, May 1, 1987.

[307] Johnson, Stephen B., *The United States Air Force and the Culture of Innovation*, Air Force Museum, 2001.

[308] Patterson, William H., *The Evolution of a New Technology Concept in the U.S.A.*, 1985.

Patterson expressed the view of many at his company, "When Si Ramo came aboard, there was a great pressure to get Convair off the program—off everything. And the idea I think behind it was they wanted to take over the whole thing."[309]

The fall of 1954 saw considerable push-back from Convair and other aviation companies, lobbying against Ramo-Wooldridge, taking out ads in magazines and newspapers, and tapping political connections in Washington. Convair announced that they were building an intercontinental rocket called Atlas, which would be self-guided and travel at more than 10,000 mph (in fact it would go 16,000).[310] The project had first been revealed in March, in the trade journals of aeronautics, but now Convair publicly staked out their central role in the ICBM project. A major trade publication, *Aviation Week*, complained in an editorial, with a thinly veiled reference to Ramo-Wooldridge Corporation:

> *Aircraft industry is growing increasingly uneasy over recent trends in the business pattern for new USAF missile developments. Aircraft Industries Assn. is considering a strong protest to the Pentagon. Big battle on upper Pentagon levels looms now between the established missile contractors and the Johnny-come-latelies in the field.[311]*

These actions infuriated General Schriever, but eventually some compromises were reached. Ramo and Wooldridge stepped down from the advisory committee to reduce the conflict of interest, and Convair became an "associate contractor" with additional responsibilities for testing and final assembly of the missile. It gave them some of the authority they would have had as prime contractor.

The most famous and controversial aspect of the Atlas design was the so-called "stainless steel balloon," its thin pressure-stabilized monocoque hull. Charlie wanted to make the tanks as light as possible, and his solution produced the highest mass ratio of any rocket ever built. He did not set out to build such a radical pressurized structure; it was the outcome of a series of logical steps of analysis and design.[312]

First was the choice of material. High skin temperature was one of the new problems presented by the high speed of an ICBM. For the 1000-mile rocket, designed in 1948, Charlie had chosen aluminum sheets as the

---

[309] Walker, Chuck, *Atlas: The Ultimate Weapon*, Apogee, 2005.
[310] "Intercontinental Rocket Reported Being Built", *New York Times*, December 17, 1954.
[311] "Missile Problems", *Aviation Week*, November 8, 1954, p 12.
[312] "Interview of Mr. K.J. Bossart by John L. Sloop," NASA, 1974.

building material of the monocoque hull. These standard "alclad" sheets of duralumin alloy were widely used for aircraft, because of their excellent strength to weight ratio. But the ICBM had to accelerate to speeds at which air friction would heat its surface as high as 700° F. Duralumin lost three quarters of its strength at that temperature, becoming almost completely annealed. During the MX-774 project, Charlie had decided that an ICBM would be made from stainless steel.[313] It also had the advantage that at the low temperature of liquid oxygen, stainless steel became stronger rather than brittle. It was a tricky material to work with, but he had learned how to handle it at E.G. Budd.

After choosing the material, the next task was static structural analysis, to determine how thick the walls must be to contain the fuel while it was just standing on the launch pad. In addition to pressure caused by the weight of the fuel, some extra tank pressure was required to prevent cavitation of the propellant at the pump inlet (the sudden drop of pressure at the suction head of the pump could boil the propellant and disrupt the pump's action). Pressure would stiffen the hull of the rocket, making it more resistant to bending or buckling. Pressure stiffening was a well-known mechanical-engineering concept, which Charlie would have learned in MIT's courses on airship design.[314]

The next problem was dynamic load analysis. Aerodynamic drag and the acceleration of the engines would induce further pressure. The guidance system would sometimes angle the missile to correct its attitude, and at extreme supersonic speed, this would generate strong torque and bending stresses in the missile body. Charlie assigned a new staff member to find the maximum dynamic pressure, the so-called "Max-Q." Using a mechanical calculator, the task took weeks, integrating the equations of motion, second by second, from launch to engine shut-down. As Charlie had guessed, the strongest dynamic load was found to be at 35,000 feet. This was also the altitude of the jet stream, with its strong wind shears. [315]

Knowing the maximum dynamic stresses on the missile, he prepared to design additional load-bearing structure. But Charlie was surprised to discover that the pressurized tank was already strong enough and rigid enough to handle the predicted flight stress. It did not require more

---

[313] MX-774 Ground-to-Ground Missile, Summary Report, Convair, December 1, 1949.

[314] Coincidentally, the Russian inventor and rocketry pioneer, Konstantin Tsiolkovsky, has also suggested shaping and pressure stiffening rockets like a dirigible, which was not surprising since he also designed metal-skinned airships. (Tsiolkovsky, K.E., "Investigation of Universal Space by Reactive Devices (1926)," *Works on Rocket Technology*, NASA TT F-243, p. 199).

[315] Martin, Richard E., "The Atlas and Centaur "Steel Balloon" Tanks: A Legacy of Karel Bossart," *AAS History Series, Vol 17*, AAS, San Diego, 1995.

thickness or internal framework. He believed in the correctness of his calculations, but there was considerable skepticism about the scheme. The head of Rocketdyne said his engines would "tear right through your Reynolds Wrap tanks" (referring to a popular brand of aluminum foil).

Not surprisingly, Ramo criticized the Atlas airframe design, characterizing it as a "big pressurized metal sack" that might collapse. He convinced the Air Force to fund an alternative ICBM program, named Titan, that had a more conservative two-stage design, in case the Atlas completely failed. At Glenn Martin Company, which would design and build the Titan, the engineers wanted to build a Bossart-style monocoque first stage. But Ramo forbade it, claiming it would be unsuitable for carrying a second stage on top of the thin pressurized tank.[316] He was later proved wrong by the successes of the Atlas/Agena and Atlas/Centaur two-stage rockets.

In a television interview, Charlie later summed up the novel weight-saving ideas in his design of Atlas:

We eliminated the propellant tanks that hold the oxidizer and the fuel, and put the fuel directly in contact with the outside skin of the rocket.

We eliminated all kinds of stiffening structural elements. The rocket, for instance, does not have the conventional stringers and frames that an aircraft structure has. The structure is dependent entirely, both for its strength and its rigidity, on internal pressure. The steel is not more than one millimeter thick. We have to maintain a small pressure in the tank, otherwise it would collapse of its own weight.

Another way we kept the weight down is by jettisoning the nose cone. As the missile reenters the atmosphere, it is subjected to very high forces and very severe heating from friction of the atmosphere. If we had to build the entire missile so it was strong enough and heat-resistant enough to take these loads and these temperatures, the weight of the missile would be prohibitive.

Through field experience with our missiles, we found out that the most unreliable phase of the rocket engine is the starting phase. And therefore, we decided that we did not want to start an engine in flight. And obviously, with the conventional way of staging, you have to start the second engine in flight. We then came to the solution of starting all engines, first stage and second stage, on the ground, which had the advantage that if one of them did not start, we could

[316] Davis Dyer, *TRW: Pioneering Technology and Innovation Since 1900*, Harvard, 1998.

shut them off and try again. This principle we called the one-and-a-half-stage, as distinct from the conventional two-stage flight.[317]

Following the theoretical studies of the stainless-steel-balloon tanks, it was necessary to do rigorous experimental testing. In 1953, Charlie visited Point Loma and began planning a structural testing facility at a site near Fort Rosecrans, about a mile south of the old MX-774 static-test site. Before their own fabrication facilities existed, they hired Solar Aircraft Company to build a 12-foot stainless steel test tank. Solar had manufactured metal aircraft, but in the post-war downturn of the aviation industry, they were surviving by making stainless steel coffins. The test tank was suspended in a derrick and instrumented with strain gauges and vibration sensors.

These tests were especially important for studying vibration, a problem with a large thin structure like the Atlas propellant tanks. A large flexible surface like the hull of the Atlas could vibrate in a number of different ways, called "modes." One family of vibrations was the bending modes, where the rocket bows this way and that. Another type of vibration was breathing modes, where the rocket bulges and constricts at different points along its length.

These were what are known as standing waves, where a whole number of wavelengths fit along the length of the rocket. For example, a "first-order" breathing mode would have the rocket bulge and contract in the middle, while the two ends contract and bulge in the opposite manner. Higher-order breathing modes would vibrate at a higher frequency with multiple bulges and contractions, alternating along the length of the hull. These modes represented ways the rocket might resonate, which could be disastrous if anything (such as the guidance system) generated forces that fed the vibration at those resonant frequencies.

The tests also revealed something not predicted by their mathematical analysis. So-called anomalous modes were discovered, where the circular cross section of the tank vibrated in rippling corrugations. When the problem of anomalous vibration modes was reported to Ramo-Wooldridge, they thought it was a matter of deep science that should be given to Caltech for lengthy research.[318] This was exactly the kind of problem that Ramo had claimed could not be handled by an aircraft company.

In the summer of 1954, Convair hired a young aerodynamicist, Dr. Marvin Stern. He had been working as an engineer at Republic (formerly

[317] Interview with Karel Jan Bossart by Jerome Verhaeghe, "Ruimtevaart," *Verover de Aarde*, Vlaamse Radio en Televisieomroeporganisatie, February 21, 1962. This was a popular science program on Flemish television.

[318] Interview with Dr. Marvin Stern, American Institute of Physics, May 1, 1987.

Seversky's company, where Charlie had briefly worked), and he earned a doctorate in mathematics at NYU, while taking classes after work. On his first day at Convair, they gave him a problem about a vibrating hollow cylinder as a theoretical exercise. He did not yet have a security clearance, so nobody told him that this was the Atlas fuel tank that he was analyzing.

Stern recognized the type of problem from the theory of elasticity, and he found a solution in a few hours, including the anomalous modes. His new boss, Hans Friedrich, was shocked to find that Stern's calculation agreed with test results from Point Loma, to within five percent. Friedrich, who had come to America with von Braun as a captured V-2 engineer, stubbornly refused to believe that the anomalous mode could be solved so quickly after all the controversy surrounding the problem.

Stern was sure his calculation was correct, and he brought his result to Charlie, whom he knew was more imaginative and open-minded. Charlie confided that Friedrich, like many of the German scientists, wanted things to be very orderly and proper, so he had a hard time accepting a surprise like this.

The Atlas project's executive management was delighted that their company had solved a scientific problem that Ramo claimed was beyond Convair's ability. They realized that the company needed its own collection of eminent scientists, to help them with highly technical problems, but also to counter the type of propaganda value of scientific authority that Ramo was using against them. They asked Stern to assemble a panel of consultants, which soon included Edward Teller, Fred Whipple, Theodore von Kármán, and Henry Kissinger (who consulted on strategic issues).[319]

Convair built two-foot diameter pressurized tanks to do destructive testing, even firing bullets into them to study how the stainless steel would fail. Charlie kept one of these tanks in his office, along with a hammer, for his favorite demo: the "hit the tank test."[320] One Ramo-Wooldridge engineer, James Fletcher, thought he might do more damage by hitting the tank with a glancing blow, but instead he sprained his wrist.

Late in November of 1954, Gardner and Schriever flew to San Diego for a meeting with Convair. Charlie had redesigned the Atlas to carry the 1500-pound warhead under development at Los Alamos. He presented a 3-engine missile, 75 feet tall, weighing 240,000 pounds. He also presented their work on guidance and nose cone design, contracts that Convair was

---

[319] Wheeler, John, Interviewed by Kenneth Ford, March 4, 1994, American Inst. of Physics.
[320] Martin, Richard E., "The Atlas and Centaur 'Steel Balloon' Tanks: A Legacy of Karel Bossart," *AAS History Series, Vol 17*, AAS, San Diego, 1995.

still hoping to get back. Schriever and his committee had decided to give the Atlas radio guidance contract to General Electric, claiming that Azusa was too complex for operational deployment. The GE system was based on the same principle of radio interferometry, but it used fewer antennas. The Azusa system was installed at Cape Canaveral, where it was successful as a rocket tracking system.

They also failed to keep the nose cone contract. In December of 1954, Ramo-Wooldridge and Sandia had designed a 3500-pound blunt reentry vehicle. Research published by the NACA laboratory in Ames reiterated what Karl Wood found years earlier, that a blunt-shaped vehicle was the best way to reenter the atmosphere. To deal with the enormous thermal load, the Sandia vehicle was a massive solid-copper heatsink that would absorb and distribute the thermal energy. The specified target approach speed was greatly reduced to accommodate the blunt reentry vehicle.

The nose cone had come full circle to a design similar to Convair's MX-774 spherical steel heatsink warhead. Charlie's team was blamed by Ramo for working on a sharp aerodynamic reentry vehicle, when in fact it had been imposed on them by the Air Force's specification of a Mach-6 impact speed.

By mid-1955, Convair executives and General Schriever and Ramo-Wooldridge had settled into a productive working arrangement. Convair was awarded contracts to design the air frame and steering control system, two problems that Charlie Bossart had already solved in innovative and successful ways. They also won the contract for the electrical system, final missile assembly and flight testing. Convair retained a fair amount of control over Atlas, while Ramo-Wooldridge enjoyed more control over the Titan missile system, which they had initiated as a back-up plan.

In June of 1955, Charlie was appointed chief engineer of the Atlas program. It may have seemed like an obvious title for him, since everyone knew he was the primary inventor of the missile. But after the drama with Ramo-Wooldridge, it was not until 1955 that it was certain that Convair would be playing a dominant role (or any role) in Atlas. The new title was in addition to his position as assistant chief engineer of Convair, a promotion he received in 1953.

Today, it is universally agreed that the technique of systems engineering was vitally important to military weapons systems, and to NASA's complex space missions.[321] As for the value of Ramo-Wooldridge, many at Convair had strong opinions about the conflict with that company. Lester Murray believed that R-W delayed the development of Atlas by their

---

[321] Johnson, Stephen B., *The United States Air Force and the Culture of Innovation*, 2002.

"incompetence and empire-building desire."[322] However, Thomas Lanphier, the Convair Vice President who oversaw Atlas, stated years afterwards that R-W significantly assisted in the project and that appointing them to oversee systems engineering was a good idea.

In later years, Charlie expressed the view that giving the guidance-system and nose cone contracts to other companies broadened the industrial base and spread the work load more efficiently.[323] But his team sometimes resented Ramo-Wooldridge for questioning every design decision they had ever made. He wrote, "It is understandable then that our men, who had built and flown missiles, did not take kindly to being second guessed by neophytes."[324] He continued to believe that his five-engine Atlas could have been operational in 1958 instead of 1959, if they had spent less time walking R-W through all their studies and redesigning a smaller missile.[325]

As Western intelligence about the Soviet missile program improved, the urgency of the Atlas project increased. By the summer of 1955, sophisticated continuous-wave radar was installed in Turkey, capable of monitoring the medium-range missile tests at Kapustin Yar. Less was known about the Soviet ICBM effort, which was not tested at that site.

On September 8, 1955, President Eisenhower and the National Security Council made the ICBM development program the "highest priority above all others."[326] General Schriever developed an aggressively telescoped project schedule that he called "concurrency." In his plan, many research and development projects occurred in parallel. This included building manufacturing plants, test stands, military launch pads, guidance systems, nose cone reentry systems, etc. Extra costs and risks were accepted to achieve the fastest possible development of Atlas.

Once Convair had the contract to do the assembly of the Atlas, they began construction of a massive factory on Kearny Mesa, just north of Montgomery Field Airport, in San Diego. Both Convair and the city had lobbied Congress for permission to build the $43 million facility. But some defense planners had wanted the facility to be farther from the coasts, out of range of submarine missile attack. Convair invested $20 million of their

---

[322] Beard, Edmund, *Developing the ICBM*, Columbia Univ. Press, NY, 1976.
[323] "Interview of Mr. K.J. Bossart by John L. Sloop," NASA, 1974.; Bossart, K.J., Letter to Edmund Beard, November, 1971.
[324] Bossart, Karel J., Letter to unknown author.
[325] "Interview of Mr. K.J. Bossart by John L. Sloop," NASA, 1974.
[326] Rosenberg, Max, *Plans and Policies for the Ballistic Missile Initial Operational Capability Program*, USAF Historical Division, Feb 1960.

own cash in the plant. By 1963, the site would employ 31,000 people, which was a major benefit to the local economy.

The town leaders knew that Charlie was the man whose persistence and ingenuity had brought this new industry to San Diego. He avoided the limelight, but he was soon too well-known and popular to go out to restaurants with his family and eat in peace.[327] After work, he focused on his home life and did little socializing outside of a small circle of friends.

Although a master of rocket engineering, he did not know how to drive a car with manual transmission. Nevertheless, he made time in his busy schedule to teach his children to drive. He also took them fishing in Mission Bay and went sailing when his schedule permitted. Dinner was always a time of stimulating conversation, and unlike his own father, Charlie encouraged the children to participate in adult discussion.

Jan and Newell became expert surfers and skin divers, and often brought lobsters or abalone home for dinner or as gifts for the neighbors. When the boys wanted a paddle board, Charlie showed them how to design and construct it in their garage, starting with a wooden frame, and then a fiberglass skin, like an aircraft fuselage. In his spare time, he designed an iceboat, which he and his sons built together. The prototype was fitted with three wheels instead of ice skates, and they took it out to Torrey Pines glider port to test it on the runway.

Charlie accepted a few invitations to civic events, such as local science fairs. His boys played in a local Little League Baseball team, and their famous father was asked to give a talk at the opening of a new field at Pacific Beach. He knew nothing whatsoever about baseball, not even how many players were on a team. "Who is this Mickey Mantle?" he asked his son. After researching the topic, he prepared a lengthy speech about the history of the game. At some point during its delivery, one of the children on the team got bored and unplugged the public address system. Immediately, someone else shouted "Let's play!" and the teams rushed out onto the field.

Since the Kearny Mesa plant would not be operational until 1958, in February of 1955, Convair emptied a wing of Plant 1 at Lindbergh Field to house the pilot construction of the Atlas. Above the assembly floor a second story was added, called "The Mezzanine," a 100,000 square-foot office space filled with drafting tables and work cubicles. Charlie was often seen there, standing over plans and diagrams and discussing the project with his engineers. Below the Mezzanine, on the factory floor, Charlie was familiar with every aspect of the Atlas assembly, and he had a friendly

---

[327] Newell Bossart, *personal communications*, 2012.

informal relationship with the workmen. As one co-worker said, they considered him "one of the boys."

Building an Atlas air-frame began with 3-foot wide rolls of type 301 stainless steel, delivered from Washington Steel Corporation of Pennsylvania. Convair purchased a Sendzimir mill, designed to cold roll the steel sheets to a desired thickness. In addition to controlling the thickness, cold rolling could double the metal's tensile strength by work hardening. In the mill, a pair of narrow rollers applied concentrated pressure to either side of the sheet as it passed between them. The narrow rollers were supported by thick rollers that provided stability and precision. Accidentally adding even a thousandth of an inch to the rocket hull would increase its weight by a hundred pounds. The thickness of the Atlas hull was carefully optimized, ranging from 0.016 inches at the top, to 0.040 at the bottom, where there was increased pressure from the accumulated weight of the fuel.

Sections of sheet steel were spot welded and seam welded to form cylindrical segments 10 feet in diameter and 3 feet tall. Then 23 of these segments were stove piped together and welded to form the hull of the rocket. The ends were capped with hemispheres made of petal-shaped sheets. In all, there were more than 100,000 spot welds in the completed structure. During fabrication, the tank was supported by a framework; but once completed, it had to be kept pressurized with nitrogen. It was kept "in stretch" as they said, or it would crumple and collapse. Furthermore, the kerosene tank had to be kept at a higher pressure (60 psi) than the liquid-oxygen tank (26 psi), to prevent buckling of the hemispherical bulkhead that separated the two propellants.

Frameworks attaching to the stainless steel tank carried the nose cone, the sustainer engine and the droppable booster engine section. On either side of the tank, two instrument pods carried the power supplies and systems for control, telemetry and guidance. The structural analysis of the rocket had to be extraordinarily exact, because Charlie reduced the load factors of the structure so far that some parts came within 90 percent of failure in the most extreme scenarios.[328]

The result was the most weight-efficient rocket ever built. The empty sustainer stage of the Atlas D weighed 5200 pounds, including the thousand-pound engine. It held 244,000 pounds of propellants, making a mass ratio of 47. By comparison, the mass ratio of the Titan first stage was only 18. Just for amusement, consider a modern 12-ounce soda, with its

[328] Hurlich, Abraham, "Metals and Fabrication Methods Used for the Atlas," *Metal Progress*, November, 1959.; Martin, Richard E., "The Atlas and Centaur "Steel Balloon" Tanks: A Legacy of Karel Bossart," *AAS History Series, Vol 17*, AAS, San Diego, 1995.

thin aluminum can weighing a half ounce, resulting in a mass ratio of 24. Furthermore, stainless steel is almost three times as dense as aluminum, making the Atlas fuel tank about six times thinner relative to a soda can.

Testing was a major part of Convair's responsibility. Once they had a complete prototype, it was mounted in a stand at Point Loma for cold testing of the complete air frame with or without engines. They filled the tanks with water or liquid nitrogen to test the structure and ran the pumps to test flow. Great volumes of liquid nitrogen pouring into the sea sent a cloud of steam high into the air. They measured the vibrational frequencies of the hull and simulated launch stress by hanging lead weights on the rocket and boosting it up a few inches with compressed air. The staging mechanism was tested by ejecting the booster engines and letting them fall into a net. A large thermal testing chamber was able to hold the entire rocket and subject it to temperatures from -65° F to +160° F.

The first phase of static firings and flight testing was done on the "A" model, a rocket with just two booster engines and no sustainer engine or booster-ejection system. Each Rocketdyne LR-89 engine developed over 150,000 pounds of thrust, burning liquid oxygen and a highly purified form of kerosene called RP-1. A completely new 60,000-pound thrust sustainer engine (the LR-105) was under development. But it would not be installed until the Atlas B series, which would be the first version of the rocket that would perform stage separation. Charlie worried that developing a new engine from scratch was a scheduling risk, but Ramo wanted an engine of exactly optimal size.[329]

The engine systems were first tested from June to November of 1956, at the "Battleship" test stand at Edwards AFB. This consisted of a heavy steel version of the rocket's propellant tanks, strong enough to survive an engine failure that might destroy the actual missile.

The airframe of the first prototype, Atlas 1A, was completed in March, 1956, and the engines and electronics installed by August. 1A was moved to the checkout station on the assembly floor and then shipped to Sycamore Canyon. There, Convair and the Army Corps of Engineers had constructed a 100-foot-tall static test stand in the pastureland northeast of San Diego. December 5 was the first hot test of the Atlas. To protect the rocket and tower from the engine exhaust, 30,000 gallons of water per minute was sprayed onto the flame deflector below the pad, and the engines were successfully fired for a few seconds.[330]

---

[329] "Interview of Mr. K.J. Bossart by John L. Sloop," NASA, 1974.
[330] Chapman, John L., *Atlas: The Story of a Missile*, Harper, New York, 1960.; Walker, Chuck, *Atlas:*

On December 21, the engines were fired a second time, but almost immediately, they exploded. The rocket and the test stand were seriously damaged by the blast and the subsequent fire. When the test conductor informed the executive manager of Atlas, the project manager Jim Dempsey brought a halt to the office Christmas party, and everyone rushed to Sycamore Canyon to inspect the damage and look at the telemetry.[331]

Fortunately, the next tests were successful. Another set of test towers had been built a few hundred miles to the north on a remote part of Edwards AFB. 2A was fired many times, for a total of almost 20 minutes. Instead of a water-cooled flame deflector below the rocket, the stand projected high over a canyon, allowing the unhindered exhaust flame to be studied. 3A was successfully tested at Sycamore Canyon.

In February 1957, Convair hosted a symposium on astronautics.[332] Marvin Stern, who was leading an effort to connect the company with the scientific community, convinced them to co-sponsor the event, along with the Air Research and Development Command (ARDC). He had been inspired by Professor von Kármán who convinced him that space exploration was an inevitable enterprise, and it was important to start engaging serious scientists and not allow "lunatics" to dominate the discourse.[333] Even with those restrictions, they admitted some 600 engineers and scientists to attend. Charlie was on vacation in Hawaii, but he got back just in time to attend the symposium.

The symposium's keynote address was given by General Schriever, "ICBM—A Step Toward Space Conquest." It was a surprisingly visionary talk. He pointed out that a missile able to carry a heavy warhead on an intercontinental ballistic trajectory could launch a lighter payload into orbit or even at escape velocity, and he brought up the possibility of adding a second stage to the Atlas. He discussed manned flights into space and sending unmanned probes to the Moon or Mars.

When the head of the Air Research and Development Command, General Gregory, was interviewed during the symposium, he indicated that they were funding studies of a Moon rocket and that one might be developed within five years. Unfortunately, the government had no interest in space exploration before the crisis of Sputnik. The Secretary of Defense, Charles Wilson, read about the interview in the newspaper the next day, and

The Ultimate Weapon, Apogee, 2005.
[331] Walker, Chuck, *Atlas: The Ultimate Weapon*, Apogee, 2005.
[332] *Vistas in Astronautics*, Pergamon, 1958.
[333] Interview with Dr. Marvin Stern, American Institute of Physics, May 1, 1987.

he lost his temper. He ordered Gregory to stop any such work on Moon rockets and never talk about space again.[334]

In March of 1957, there was a major reorganization, with the creation of Convair Astronautics. In 1953, Convair had been purchased from Floyd Odlum by the General Dynamics holding company (owners of Canadair and Electric Boat). Most of Convair's business involved military aircraft and a new jet airliner project that was competing with the Boeing 707. It was obvious that rocket technology had progressed from experimental to a serious business, so it was made a full-fledged division of Convair.

With the corporate upgrade of the missile division came a round of promotions. Charlie was promoted to Technical Director of Convair Astronautics, and he reported as an assistant to the vice president of engineering. His position was designed to tap his technical creativity, with the authority to monitor many projects, suggest ideas, help with solutions to problems and raise a red flag if he saw something that might be wrong. Of course, Atlas was the most important work in the division, and Charlie continued to oversee its progress in detail.

Stepping into Charlie's old job as chief engineer was Mort Rosenbaum. He had also replaced Charlie as Atlas project engineer, the last time they were promoted. Before the missile project, Rosenbaum had distinguished himself at Convair, working on the B-24 Liberator and the B-36 intercontinental bomber.

Charlie was never interested in being an executive manager. That role was played by Jim Dempsey, who was promoted to manager of Convair Astronautics. The next year, he was also elevated to the level of vice president at Convair. Dempsey was a West Point graduate and a P-38 photo-reconnaissance pilot in the Second World War. Promoted to Lt. Colonel, he became the Air Force's range operations officer at Cape Canaveral until joining Convair in 1953. With his Air Force experience in guided missiles, he had been assigned as program director of Atlas in 1954.

By December 1956, the first flight-test vehicle, Atlas 4A, was completed and ready to ship to Cape Canaveral, Florida. It was too big to ship by air, so a 20-man convoy drove it from San Diego to the Cape. A specially designed trailer held the support cradle that the missile was built on at the factory, cloaked with a nylon security cover. Driving only during the daytime, the trip took nine days. At the rocket's maximum speed of 16,000 mph, it would have taken eight minutes.

---

[334] "Rocket Around the Moon Expected Within 5 Years," *New York Times*, March 3, 1957.; Interview with Dr. Marvin Stern, American Institute of Physics, May 1, 1987.

At Cape Canaveral, Convair had a presence since 1954, when they had set up their Azusa tracking system.[335] Coupled with an IBM 704 computer, the system was used for tracking and impact-prediction on Redstone, Snarks and other missiles. Convair had originally hoped to use Azusa as the radio guidance system for Atlas, but it was still used to track the missile's trajectory. The General Electric radio guidance system was similar in principle to Azusa. Located at the Guided Missile Control Facility, it used a Burroughs computer to do impact prediction. In addition to those systems, the Atlas was tracked by a third radar station located on the roof of the control center, an updated version of the SCR-584, which could "skin track" the rocket from the radar reflecting off its metal hull. In contrast, the GE and Azusa systems used an active transponder on the missile that echoed a signal back to the radar, which greatly extended their range.[336]

Atlas would require hundreds of Convair employees at the Cape. To manage operations, they sent Byron G. MacNabb, a colorful and energetic man who had overseen hydrogen bomb testing in the South Pacific before joining Convair. When he arrived at the Cape in August 1955, he found "acres of rattle-snakes." His first task was the construction of four new launch complexes, more sophisticated than the simple concrete slabs used to launch Snark cruise missiles (so many of them had crashed into the Atlantic, men joked about the "Snark-infested waters").

Atlas launch complexes LC-11 through LC-14 came to be known as "ICBM row." In addition they would need facilities for storing fuel, generating liquid oxygen, and blockhouses able to withstand a launch-pad explosion. Fully filled Atlas tanks had been detonated on Edwards AFB at a special high-risk test site, to measure the explosive force of a worst-case accident. To withstand such blasts, MacNabb built domed blockhouses with reinforced concrete five feet thick, covered with ten feet of sand.

Cape Canaveral was a five-mile-wide triangular sand-bar off the coast of Florida. Much of it was covered with palmetto scrub and infested with scorpions and venomous snakes, which formed a natural security barrier.[337] South of the Cape, the small resort town of Cocoa Beach was spread along a strip of land only a few blocks wide, between the Atlantic Ocean and the Banana River. No place in the town or the Cape was more than a dozen feet above sea level. MacNabb met with the city council to help (sometimes coerce) them to expand its borders and utility services for the impending

---

[335] The Air Force was evaluating Azusa versus General Electric's phase comparison radar, starting with tests on Redstone missiles. Eventually, they chose GE for the guidance of Atlas.

[336] The signal strength from reflected radar falls off as the 4th power of the range, while a transponder signal falls off as the square of the range.

[337] Hunter, Mel, *The Missilemen*, Doubleday, 1960.

influx of personnel. Part of the territory annexed by the town was a housing development that General Dynamics funded. Still called Convair Cove today, it has street names such as Dempsey Drive and MacNabb Parkway.[338]

The launch complexes and tracking stations of the Cape were only one part of the Atlantic Missile Range. To the Southeast, a string of radar and telemetry stations was constructed on islands in the Caribbean and Atlantic, able to track and receive telemetry along the flight path. At maximum range, an ICBM test ended in a splashdown near Ascension Island in the South Atlantic. However, the experimental model-A rocket, with just two boosters and no sustainer engine, was designed to fly only 500 nautical miles.

Early in June, 1957, Charlie and his team were at Cape Canaveral to observe the first test flight of Atlas. They stayed at the Starlite Motel, a futuristic Googie-style building with its famous rocket-shaped neon sign. It had been constructed at the behest of MacNabb, when he discovered there was a shortage of hotels in town.

The manager of the Starlite was Henri Landwirth who, Charlie was surprised to learn, also came from Antwerp. But Henri's childhood had been drastically different. When he was 13, the Nazis executed his parents and sent him to Auschwitz. He survived the camps and after the war he got a job as a crewman on a ship from Antwerp to New York City. MacNabb got to know him when he was managing a hotel in Miami and invited him to run the new Starlite. Landwirth added one Belgian touch to the motel: a replica of *Mannekin Pis*, a famous statue in Brussels of a baby boy peeing into a fountain. The interior décor included murals of space scenes and black lights.

Henri was popular with the Air Force and Convair personnel, and a couple years later, Walter Cronkite and the Mercury astronauts also chose the Starlite as their home base.[339] Few people brought their families to Cocoa Beach, which in those days was a somewhat seedy neighborhood full of strip clubs and gambling parlors. Many of the young men staying at the Cape worked hard and played hard, and Henri supported their lifestyle. The Starlite was known for its parties and pranks. It was not unusual for people to get thrown fully clothed into the pool, and the astronaut Alan Shepard once put an alligator in it.

The motel's cocktail lounge was one of the busiest bars in town—a town that already had a lot of bars. One drink, the "Atlas Special," had a

---

[338] "The History of Cocoa Beach, Florida," www.cityofcocoabeach.com.; "MacNabb Leaves After Eight Years," *Daytona Beach Morning Journal, August 17, 1963*.
[339] Thompson, Neal, *Light This Candle: The Life and Times of Alan Shepard*, Three Rivers, 2004.; "Henri Landwirth, www.gktw.org.

sufficient alcohol content to be lit on fire before it was served. One evening, perhaps after a few Atlas Specials, Charlie and Bill Patterson decided to prank Landwirth by temporarily kidnapping his *Mannekin Pis* statue.

At launch complex LC-14, Atlas 4A had been erected on March 21, 1957, and it was briefly fired in a static test on June 3. When Atlas rockets arrived at the Cape, they came with a collection of spare parts and a list of problems found at the inspection bay in San Diego. The thin stainless steel skin had to be examined inch by inch to make sure there were no dents or damage during transit. After the cross-country truck ride, they sometimes even found bullet holes in Atlas tanks, and the crew had to develop a way to patch them.[340]

The Convair crew worked for months to prepare 4A, with growing pressure to launch. MacNabb proposed a launch date of June 15, but made it clear he wanted more time. Dempsey told him, by the 15th, either the missile would be fired, or he would be. Fortunately, they were ready a few days before the deadline.[341]

On June 11, the flight-test countdown and preparation began before sunrise. At the southern end of the Cape, a red canvas ball was hoisted on a 90-foot pole, a traditional warning to ships that the coastal waters were restricted for military operations. It was also a signal to the townsfolk and journalists in Cocoa Beach to watch for a launch. Before dawn, the launch control crew arrived at the Cape on blue Air Force buses, but Convair VIPs like Charlie had company cars and arrived later in the morning.

The Blockhouse was 750 feet from the launch pad, but like the one at White Sands, it was not a good place to watch the launch. Inside, technicians could see the rocket only on television screens or through periscopes. After greeting people and visiting for a while, Charlie left the blockhouse and watched the test from the control center, 9000 feet west of the pad. Another popular place for viewing Atlas launches was the roof of Hangar J, Convair's base of operations at the Cape.

Loading the liquid oxygen tanks began an hour before take-off. As the pale blue liquid cooled pumps and pipes to -297° F, a distinctive wailing sound was generated by the liquid. LOX was a quirky and dangerous substance that had to be handled carefully. It was denser than water and much more compressible, and it was prone to cavitation and "water-hammer" shocks that could travel through the plumbing, bursting pipes and

---

[340] O'Donnell, Franklin, *The Venus Mission*, JPL, 2012.
[341] Walker, Chuck, *Atlas: The Ultimate Weapon*, Apogee, 2005.

valves. If it leaked, it pooled in low places and created fire hazards. In the humid Florida climate, the thin uninsulated steel walls of the oxidizer tank accumulated as much as 400 pounds of ice, an unwanted extra payload that would hopefully shake loose as soon as the rocket lifted off.[342]

Even though the rocket was made from stainless steel, the humidity and salt spray at the Cape was a concern. Before launch, the rocket was sprayed with a mixture of mineral oil and petroleum spirits, developed by the Atlas project as a "water displacement" treatment. It evaporated to leave a thin protective film on the metal surfaces. The product was later marketed as the popular WD-40.

At 2:37 pm, the engines were ignited. Clamps held the rocket down for 11 seconds, until full thrust was developed. Charlie had taken particular care about how to release the rocket smoothly, without jolting its structure. The flight began perfectly, with stable yaw, pitch and roll. But at 24 seconds, one of the engines failed. The control system struggled to compensate for the lopsided thrust, and a couple seconds later the second engine stopped. The rocket gyrated and turned over, then began a nose dive. At 50.7 seconds, the range safety officer sent the self-destruct command, and an explosive charge went off next to the bulkhead between the oxygen and fuel tanks. The missile was blasted apart at 10,000 feet, raining burning debris on the beach and the waters off the coast. Immediately, the analysis of telemetry began, and every piece that could be salvaged was collected for study. They found evidence that some cables and pipes in the tail section were burned during the flight.

Although the rocket failed to complete its flight, the test achieved 90 percent of its objectives. Most of the rocket's systems behaved normally before the malfunction of the engines.[343] There was one particular triumph in the test; Charlie's controversial steel-balloon airframe had performed beyond expectations. Until the self-destruct charge blew it apart, the missile structure showed no signs of failure. The engine malfunction caused the rocket to perform radical maneuvers, flying sideways at over 300 miles per hour, and then doing a complete loop-the-loop. It experienced aerodynamic stress far beyond its design limitations. One expert estimated it underwent a 3g transverse overload, which solid-framework structures such as the Thor or von Braun's Jupiter would not have survived.[344]

After reviewing the failure of 4A and making some changes to the next rocket, the second attempt to launch Atlas came in September. On the 20th,

[342] "Flight Test P4-103-00-04," Convair Astronautics (film of the Atlas 4A launch).
[343] *Atlas, The ICBM*, U.S. Air Force, film SFP 583.
[344] Martin, Richard E., "The Atlas and Centaur "Steel Balloon" Tanks: A Legacy of Karel Bossart," *AAS History Series, Vol 17*, AAS, San Diego, 1995.

it was statically fired for 36 seconds on the launch pad. In the early afternoon of the 25th, Atlas 6A took off from Cape Canaveral. Thirty-three seconds into the flight, the fuel pump lost power, and the engines shut down a few seconds later. The rocket coasted to an altitude of 14,300 feet and was commanded to self-destruct half a minute later.

In these early days, it often took two tries to fix a problem: one launch to discover it, and a second to test several different theories about what was causing it. The propellant pumps in the Atlas were driven by a 10,000 rpm gas turbine, powered by the rocket's fuel. Analysis of the debris from the July launch showed that pipes and electrical cables had been burned by the turbine exhaust. An aluminum barrier installed in the engine compartment of 4A and 6A was insufficient, and the same burn-through problem occurred again. But this time, extra telemetry sensors were able to confirm what the exact problem was.[345]

While Charlie and his team studied the results of 4A's flight, they were only partly aware of how close the race was with their Soviet counterparts. They had been shown intelligence on the Russian missile program, and they were asked to design a best guess of what a Soviet ICBM would look like. Charlie predicted it would be a massive rocket, but its construction was well within the realm of possibility.[346]

The first launch of the R-7 took place on May 15, a month before the Atlas flight test, but a fire in the engine compartment caused it to crash a few hundred miles from the launch pad. When the American ICBM also failed, Korolev was relieved, because it demonstrated to his leadership how difficult the long-range rocket problem was.

The Soviet Union did not have the resources to miniaturize their warhead and repeatedly redesign the rocket. Comparable in size to Charlie's early seven-engine MX-1593, the Soviet missile had a fully-fueled weight of 615,000 pounds and an 11,000-pound payload capacity. The R-7 was a parallel-stage design, with a central sustainer and four cone-shaped lateral boosters that dropped off when they were used up. Made from aluminum-magnesium alloy, the design was not as radical as Charlie's steel balloon, but one clever idea saved structural weight. Most rockets rest on their base when they are erected on the launch pad, and the lower section must be strong enough to support the entire weight of the rocket. But the R-7 was suspended from its middle before launch, so no part of it had to bear more than half the weight of the rocket.

---

[345] Chapman, John L., *Atlas: The Story of a Missile*, Harper, 1960.
[346] Patterson, William H., *The Evolution of a New Technology Concept in the U.S.A.*, 1985.

After two failed launches, the R-7 was successful on August 21, traveling from Tyura-Tam in Kazakhstan (later named Baikonur), across the length of the Soviet Union. The telemetric nose cone, filled with sensors, vacuum tube electronics and radio gear, was vaporized in a ball of fire as it reentered the atmosphere over the Kamchatka peninsula. The race for the first intercontinental rocket was won by the Russians, and it would be one year before Atlas flew to its full 5500-mile range. However, the Soviets had not yet solved the heat-shield problem; they could not yet deliver a thermonuclear warhead with the R-7. Their warhead was a sharp-nosed cone, and they soon adopted a blunt-nosed design and an ablative heat shield.

While Sergei Korolev and the Soviet missile program were cloaked in secrecy, the Atlas was more public, and the Russians benefited from espionage to an unknown extent. They hoped to build a guidance system based on microwave interferometry and controlled by a digital computer, just like Azusa. However, they lacked the technology to build either of those components.[347] Instead R-7 was guided by a massive analog computer and a mechanically scanning radio beam.

Before the third Atlas test could take place, a pivotal event occurred that would change the perception of rocketry and space exploration at all levels of society and government: the launch of Sputnik.

The U.S. began serious planning for a satellite mission in 1955. They considered four satellite projects for the upcoming International Geophysical Year (a multinational scientific initiative to explore the Earth, oceans, and upper atmosphere). The Army proposed Project Orbiter, using von Braun's Redstone/Jupiter-C missile with extra stages. The Navy was building their own rocket, the Vanguard. The Air Force submitted a plan for a satellite launched by Atlas A combined with a second stage. In addition, Convair Astronautics presented its own private satellite project called the Orbital Research and Test Vehicle (ORTV), a 500-pound satellite to be launched by Atlas C.

Representatives from the Navy's Vanguard project and General Electric Corporation (Vanguard's rocket-engine contractor) campaigned against von Braun's Project Orbiter and the Atlas-based satellite projects. GE's Richard Porter chaired the American satellite committee and promoted the idea that the first U.S. satellite should not be launched by a military missile. The Navy's Vanguard was purely a scientific rocket.

---

[347] Lipkin, I.A., *Istoriya Sozdaniya Otechestvennykh Sistem Radioupravleniya* (History of Domestic Radio Remote Control Systems), 2001.

Privately, they undermined the Army plan by suggesting that the first American satellite should not be made by former Nazis. Eventually the Navy won the day. Von Braun was forbidden from orbiting a satellite in September of 1956, when he had a rocket prepared to do so.[348]

July of 1957 was the beginning of IGY. On July 18, Charlie attended a symposium on rockets and satellites in Cranfield, England. He took his daughter Marion with him on that trip, and they spent a week touring London, and then flew to Antwerp to visit Aunt Vire and Daisy. Belgian and American cousins would not meet again until Charlie's son, Newell and his family visited, in 1988.

At the conference, Milton Rosen from the Naval Research Lab described the American satellite launcher, Vanguard. Charlie gave a technically advanced talk on rocket structure, flight control and how those problems scaled with increasing size.[349]

Soviet professor Boris Petrov submitted a paper on instrumentation for a large complex scientific satellite. The satellite that he described would eventually be launched as Sputnik-3, but when the R-7 was ready, Petrov's satellite was a year behind schedule. Korolev did not want to wait; he was sure the Americans were going to launch a satellite any day. He ordered his engineers to prepare *Prosteishy Sputnik* ("simple satellite").

Despite numerous announcements of the Soviet Union's intent to launch a satellite, most experts were caught off-guard on October 4. The simple satellite was a 184-pound aluminum sphere, containing a battery-powered radio beacon. It orbited the Earth every 92 minutes, transmitting its famous "beep beep beep".[350] Even Soviet leadership was surprised by the psychological impact of the first artificial Earth satellite. Premier Khrushchev's attitude toward space exploration quickly changed from indifference to enthusiasm, as did that of many American politicians.

More disturbing to military experts was the seven-ton sustainer stage that was tumbling in orbit, right behind Sputnik. It was a sobering demonstration of the rocket's power, obviously much bigger than Atlas. While the satellite itself was barely visible to the naked eye, everyone could see the giant rocket stage, like a bright star passing overhead.

Delighted by Sputnik's popularity and propaganda value, Khrushchev gave Korolev only weeks to prepare a second satellite for orbit, to mark the 50th anniversary of the communist revolution. This time the satellite would

---

[348] Pearson, Drew, Jack Anderson, *U.S.A.: Second-Class Power?*, Simon & Schuster, 1958.

[349] Bossart, K.J., "Design Problems of Large Rockets," *High Altitude and Satellite Rockets, Cranfield Symposium*, July 18-20, 1957.

[350] Sputnik transmitted pulses of unmodulated carrier wave. The famous beeping sound was actually generated by heterodyning in the radio receivers.

contain a live dog. Sputnik-2 was hastily assembled from a spare copy of Sputnik-1 and a dog cabin used in high-altitude research rockets. These were fastened to the nose of the sustainer stage and remained attached to the rocket (unlike like Sputnik-1, which had been ejected from the rocket stage by a pneumatic piston).

In the early morning of November 3, a captured Moscow street dog named Laika became the first living creature to orbit in outer space. Unfortunately, after a few hours the cabin temperature rose to 109° F, and the dog became comatose from heatstroke. She died within the next few orbits, but the Soviet news agency kept that a secret and continued for several days to give false reports of the dog's condition.[351]

America's first response to Sputnik was the attempted launch of the Navy's Vanguard satellite. On December 6, the rocket rose a few feet and then collapsed and exploded in a ball of flames. The next day, the public saw the catastrophic newsreel footage; papers dubbed it "Kaputnik." The exact cause of the failure was never determined with certainty. Eventually a tiny three-pound Vanguard satellite was placed in orbit, but only on the third attempt. A dozen Vanguard rockets were launched, with only four successes. The humiliating failures effectively ended the Navy's space rocket program and knocked them out of the competition with the Army and Air Force.

After the two unsuccessful Atlas tests, Convair's engineers were sure they had fixed the problem with the turbine exhaust by adding a three-inch thick fiberglass shield in the engine compartment and diverting the turbine exhaust to the side. The problem had not been caught during static testing because the deluge of water used to cool the launch pads had also cooled the engine compartment.

Another improvement exemplified the sophisticated engineering problems that Charlie considered. Having reduced the weight of the rocket so radically, he was concerned about oscillation of the thin flexible structure. On the 4A flight, telemetry revealed a 17 Hz third-order bending mode in the tank. Third-order means the middle and ends bend one way while the two regions between are bending the other way. The vibration was not strong enough to be a concern unless the guidance system interpreted the bending as a course deviation and swiveled the engines at

---

[351] *Sovetsky Kosmos*, Archive of the President of the Russian Federation, 2010. (a collection of classified Red TASS articles on the Soviet space program).; Malashenkov, D.S., "Some Unknown Pages of the Living Organisms' First Orbital Flight", 34th COSPAR, Houston, 2002.

the same frequency. If that happened, the feedback would cause the bending oscillation to grow larger until the rocket was damaged.

To avoid that potential problem, low-frequency-pass filters were added to the control circuits, preventing the engines from swiveling faster than 4 times per second.[352] Another dynamic effect was sloshing of fuel in the tank, which could also start feedback with the guidance system. In analyzing it, Charlie knew that sloshing liquid was described by the same mathematics as a swinging pendulum.[353] Ring-shaped baffles in the fuel tank would dampen the movement of the liquid, and vertical baffles would prevent the formation of a vortex as the fuel was pumped out.

That fall, reporters in Cocoa Beach could see two Atlas missiles on their launch pads. They had been erected in November and undergone brief static tests; but launching was delayed, probably so President Eisenhower could announce the launch while he was attending the NATO conference in Paris.[354] After the success of the Soviet ICBM and two satellites, and the embarrassing failure of Vanguard, U.S. allies were anxious about the apparent superiority of Russian rocket technology. The prestige of Convair was also on the line, with critics glad to step in if the Atlas failed for a third time.

The missile 10A had been ready to go on launch complex LC-12, but technical problems led to scrubbing its flight. 12A was set up on LC-14, so it was decided to launch it the next day, December 17. Some of the crew began launch preparations as early as 2:30 am. The public was alerted to a rocket launch at 8:15 that morning, when the red ball was hoisted at the Cape. The stainless steel missile was clearly visible from the northern shore, which was soon crowded with spectators. Around 10:30, they could see the plumes of vapor from liquid oxygen pumping into the rocket.

The missile lifted off 39 minutes after noon. It rose vertically to 15,000 feet and began pitching over to the southeast. The engines burned for their full 125 seconds. As the missile moved outside the range of the radars at the Cape, reports came in over undersea cable from observation posts along the path. The crew in the blockhouse waited anxiously for seven minutes, until splash down was confirmed 490 nautical miles from the launch pad, between San Salvador and Mayaguana islands. Then the cheering began.

In Paris, Eisenhower was pleased and relieved to hear the news of the successful ICBM test. In Cocoa Beach, the crew popped open the champagne and threw a celebration party at the Starlite Motel. MacNabb

---

[352] Walker, Chuck, *Atlas: The Ultimate Weapon*, Apogee, 2005.
[353] Bossart, K.J., "Design Problems of Large Rockets," *High Altitude and Satellite Rockets, Cranfield Symposium*, July 18-20, 1957.
[354] "Atlas Test Likely Before Thursday," *New York Times*, Dec 15, 1957.

was hoisted on people's shoulders and carried around the banquet room. One rather critical local journalist had made a running joke of growing his beard until the Atlas had a successful launch, and he was shaved somewhat unceremoniously after he arrived at the party.

When Charlie showed up, his friends called "Congratulations! Long live Mister Atlas!" He thanked them and said, "This job was too big for one man. There are thousands and thousands of Mister Atlases." Someone in the room shouted, "But there is only one Charlie Atlas!"[355]

The Atlas rocket was in the news fairly frequently, and Charlie was getting more publicity as its chief designer. A week after the 12A launch, he appeared on the TV game show, *What's My Line?* The game had a panel of celebrities who asked questions and tried to guess the occupation of a contestant. Knowing he was from San Diego, the panelists guessed his job fairly quickly, asking if he worked for Convair, and learning it was not an airplane project. After his job as designer of ballistic missiles was revealed, the book publisher Bennett Cerf was eager to ask questions about space travel:

"Mister Bossart, when are we going to hit the Moon?"

"It may not be very long," Charlie replied, "I think it will be possible in one or two years."

Cerf added, "That's to hit the Moon, not to take a passenger up there?"

Charlie agreed, "Oh no, that's quite a different problem!"

The host joked, "You know Cerf wants to sell his books everywhere!"[356]

Charlie donated his game winnings of $50 to the San Diego Red Cross. Watching their father on television, his children noticed for the first time that their father spoke with an accent.

At Kearny Mesa, the 252-acre Atlas plant was ready for use by February of 1958, and an official dedication ceremony was held in July. The new facility and its economic impact on the community had been big news in San Diego, and 97,000 people showed up for the outdoor portion of the event. Dempsey introduced California Governor Goodwin Knight, who gave the opening address. Next, Charlie Bossart was presented with the Air Force Exceptional Civilian Service Award. He gave a humble and moving speech about America and the privilege of citizenship.

The beautiful new office buildings, designed by the architects Pereira & Luckman, were a response to criticism that the aircraft industry treated its

---

[355] *Air & Space*, June/July 1980.; *Time*, December 30, 1957., De Bruyn, F., *De Klap Op De Vuurpijl*, Vol 11, No. 10, Antwerp, 1964.

[356] *What's My Line?*, CBS, Season 9, Episode 17, December 22, 1957.

engineers and scientists like blue-collar factory workers.[357] Its most iconic feature was a 245-foot-long helical ramp, from the lobby of the reception center to the second floor, hanging from the ceiling by stainless steel rods over a circular pool. The spiraling ramp represented the dream of orbiting into space. During the indoor reception, the ramp became packed with visitors, and some of the engineers speculated about how much stress the structure could withstand.

In front of the reception center, a reflecting pool also acted as a 40,000-gallon reservoir for the plant's fire-fighting system. Behind the reception center and office buildings, were 292,000 square feet of laboratories, computer centers and engineering space, in a complex of crisscrossing buildings called "the waffle." Further back, the primary rocket-assembly area was building No. 5, a 580,000-square-foot open space.

The next step in flight testing was the Atlas B, a complete long-range version of the one-and-a-half-stage rocket, with a central sustainer engine, jettisoned boosters, and a separable nose cone. Based on their experience with the tests of Atlas A, the model B had a lighter hull with thinner stainless steel skin. Static testing of 1B began in January 1958 at Sycamore Canyon. The first flight test at the Cape was 3B, on July 19. Unfortunately, 22 seconds after lift-off, a rate gyro failed and the rocket began to hunt, weaving from side to side, until the range safety officer sent the self-destruct command at 54 seconds.

On August 2, 1958, Atlas 4B became the first successful test of America's ICBM, performing its long-range flight program. Once the rocket lifted off from launch complex LC-13, responsibility passed from the blockhouse crew to the control center. There, two large pen plotters drew paths on maps of the test range. One drew the position of the missile as reported by the radar, and the other drew the computer-predicted impact point (where it would land if the missile's engine were to stop at that moment). The range safety office kept a careful eye on the impact predictor plot, making sure it never moved outside the flight corridor.

4B rose vertically for ten or twelve seconds, rolling to face the target azimuth.[358] Next it tilted briefly and allowed gravity to pitch the missile toward the target. The first milestone of the flight was booster shutdown at 128 seconds and the successful dropping of the 6700-pound tail assembly and engines. The tail section with the booster engines amounted to almost

[357] Hughes, Thomas P., *Rescuing Prometheus*, Pantheon, 1998.
[358] The Russian R-7's launch pad was on a giant turn-table, which was rotated before take-off, to set the rocket's azimuth.

half the structural weight of the Atlas. The sustainer stage was mostly made up of the light-weight steel balloon tanks. At 254 seconds, the sustainer engine shut down. The small roll-stabilization engines continued to burn for about 25 seconds to fine-tune the missile's velocity. The last milestone of the test was passed when the nose cone separated successfully.

The first few tests were fueled for only half the maximum range, and 4B traveled about 2500 miles. The nose cone reentered the atmosphere at 21 times the speed of sound. A 16,000° F bow shockwave formed in front of the nose cone, the thermal energy absorbed by a blunt heat shield contained 1115 pounds of copper. It was a sufficient mass to absorb the reentry heat without reaching the melting point.

Up until then, the GE radio guidance system tracked the missile, but only the onboard gyros controlled guidance. This was adequate for testing the propulsion systems but not accurate enough to meet Air Force targetting specifications. On Atlas 5B (August 28) the radio guidance system was finally allowed to actively control the missile, measuring the missile's trajectory, and sending commands to steer it and turn off the engines when it reached a precisely determined speed. As the stages of testing continued, the Atlas ICBM was becoming fully operational.[359]

The first full-distance test of the Atlas came on November 28, 1958. 12B was allowed to fly 5506 nautical miles, landing in the middle of the South Atlantic. 12B was one of a few "hotrod" versions of the B series, with a hollow pointed nose cone and lighter instruments that were being developed for the next test series. The press reported the flight the next day. By then the Atlas project was far from being a secret. After the tight security was lifted, Charlie told reporters, "I would have liked to have told you about everything, but I wasn't tempted even once."

Atlas C was the last test series of Charlie's missile, very close to the production model. It contained some improvements in the accuracy of its guidance systems, and weight was reduced further by making the stainless steel hull thinner, replacing some of the aluminum tail section with fiberglass, and optimizing the instrumentation to almost half the weight of the electronics in the B series.

Neither the guidance system nor the nose cone was ideal in Atlas. The copper heat-sink was far too heavy, and the radio guidance system placed many constraints on the deployment of Atlas. In particular, only one missile at a time could be launched, since the radio system could not control more than one missile at a time. Prof. Draper at MIT had been advocating pure

---

[359] "Ten Crucial Years," *Air Force Space Digest*, May, 1964.

inertial guidance, using his new high-precision gyroscopes that floated in liquid. General Electric and AVCO were researching an ablative heat shield that used lightweight plastic.[360] This would protect the warhead by charring and flaking away in thin layers during reentry.

In the summer of 1957, von Kármán chaired a conference of 30 scientists (including three Nobel Prize laureates) at Woods Hole. General Schriever dropped in one day, bringing Simon Ramo with him. At the time, not just Convair was clashing with Ramo-Wooldridge over project management. Tempers flared when Ramo suggested an initiative to use inertial guidance instead of radio and improving the nose cone by using ablation.

Draper from MIT stood up and said, "Aren't you the one that stopped work on the high precision inertial navigation components in favor of radio guidance?"

Arthur Kantrowitz from AVCO stood up and said, "Aren't you the one who inhibited work on an ablating nose cone because you wanted a solid heat sink?"

Convair's Marvin Stern also chastised Ramo. Referring to his famous criticism of Convair, "You're now talking about an order of magnitude improvement in accuracy. What I want to know is, have you reconsidered your original argument, or have you upped the number of Nobel Prizes?"[361]

Atlas D was the first model deployed as an ICBM and used extensively for space flights. Six of these missiles were operational in October of 1959, each carrying a 1.44-megaton W-49 warhead. Eventually 30 fully-armed Atlas D's were deployed. In the military installations, one radio guidance system was associated with three missiles. The first deployed Atlas D's at Vandenberg AFB were in open launch pads with no protection.

The Atlas D was considerably more powerful than Atlas B. Lighter weight and improvements in the thrust and exhaust velocity of Rocketdyne's engines allowed Atlas 56D to fly 7859 nautical miles, from Cape Canaveral to the Indian Ocean southeast of Cape Town.[362] This beat the Soviet record of an R-7A missile, which had flown 6700 nautical miles and landed in the Pacific Ocean south of Hawaii.

---

[360] Sutton, George W., "The Initial Development of Ablation Heat Protection," *JBIS,* 2006. At high temperatures, phenolic resins (like Bakelite) turned to charcoal and gas rather than melting.

[361] Stern, Marvin, *Selected Memories of a Defense Dilettante,* Xlibris, 2001.; Interview with Dr. Marvin Stern, American Institute of Physics, May 1, 1987.

[362] It's not obvious looking at a map, but a straight (great-circle) route exists from Florida to as far as Australia entirely over water.

In 1961, 27 Atlas E missiles were deployed by the Air Force. They contained the final solution to the guidance and reentry problem. Replacing the complicated radio guidance system was a self-contained gyro-stabilized platform.[363] It contained a solid-state digital computer only two feet wide, which was a technological marvel at the time. The newly developed 3.75-megaton W-38 warhead was housed in a nose cone built by AVCO. It used a phenolic resin ablative heat shield, weighing 1300 pounds less than the old copper nose cone. The model E missiles were installed in protective "coffins," stored horizontally. Heavy doors would roll back, and the missile would rise to vertical launch position, but it was then vulnerable for several minutes while it was being fueled.

Charlie witnessed the last test of his ICBM at the Cape, Atlas 21F, in December of 1962.[364] The Atlas F was the final version of the operational ICBM, almost the same as the model E, but it was modified to be fueled while in a hardened underground silo. The missile took off at 4:26 in the afternoon, and plunged into the Atlantic 30 minutes later, near the Ascension Island tracking station. It was the 151st launch of an Atlas, and the 11th success in a row. In all, 108 had been successful thus far, with most of the failures occurring earlier in the test program.

"It so happens that politics wasn't, and never has been, my forte," Charlie wrote to the author Edmund Beard.[365] While he loved the technical work of designing a missile, he was mindful of the political and strategic context of the ICBM. He admired the freedom of American society, and he hated the authoritarianism that he had seen first-hand in Europe and which communism represented.

Near the end of 1957, one incident exemplified his views. His teenage sons had just returned from an afternoon of surfing and were cleaning up for dinner, when they heard their father raising his voice in the other room, "You get out of my house!"

Charlie never yelled at anyone, and the boys ran out to see what was wrong. A man at the door was saying, "Listen Bossart, you have to sign this if you want to keep your job," demanding that he sign a loyalty oath as part of his new security clearance. Charlie told him how much he loved this country and that he came to America to get away from just this sort of nonsense. "If my word is not enough, get somebody else to build your

---

[363] MacKenzie, Donald, *Inventing Accuracy*, MIT, 1990.
[364] "Final Shot is Fired in Atlas Research," *New York Times*, Dec 6, 1962.; AP photo of Bossart at the test.
[365] Karel J. Bossart, *letter to Edmund Beard*, November 1971.

rocket!" The man stubbornly refused to leave, until Jan and Newell helped him out the door and tossed him into the hedge.

Despite the man's threat, nobody ever suggested that Charlie Bossart be replaced or lose his security clearance.[366] He was universally admired and trusted. But it was an era of political repression. In contrast, Dr. Edward Condon, another pioneer of American guided missiles during WWII, repeatedly lost and regained his security clearance, because of his political conflicts with Joe McCarthy and Richard Nixon.[367]

Charlie viewed the ICBM as a deterrent, not a weapon of aggression. One of his colleagues said, "Charlie Bossart is a practical, scientific peace monger."[368] Charlie himself said, "My greatest satisfaction in working on the Atlas is that it may stop killing." He was skeptical that the Soviets had large numbers of missiles, and believed they were too rational and valued life too much to start a nuclear war. Many of those working on the ICBM saw it like Charlie, as balance and deterrent. However, there were some hawks. For example, John von Neumann, who had chaired the Teapot Committee, thought war with Russia was inevitable and once said, "If you say why not bomb them tomorrow, I say why not today? If you say today at 5 o'clock, I say why not 1 o'clock?"[369]

Charlie and his team were instrumental in creating the mechanism of deterrence that prevented nuclear war by making it unwinnable. The two ICBM systems, in the United States and the Soviet Union, came online as battle-ready weapons at about the same time: Atlas in late 1959 and the R-7 in 1960. The work Charlie had done since 1946, and during the period without government support, allowed America to build the Atlas in only four years, once it became an emergency project.

One can only speculate what might have happened without his engineering and strategic insights. The Titan missile, which was a project started from scratch and built by another aircraft company with less prior experience, was not operational until 1962. Without Atlas, Titan would have left a dangerous imbalance of power, with the Russians, who were two years ahead in deploying a missile. However, without Convair's advocacy and research on long-range rockets, it is possible that the Titan would have taken even longer to develop. If the most conservative forces had prevailed, an American ICBM program might not have begun in earnest until the country was shocked into action by the launch of Sputnik.

[366] Karel Jan Bossart Jr., Newell Bossart, *personal communications*, 2012.
[367] Morse, Philip M., *Edward Uhler Condon 1902-1974*. National Academy of Sciences, 1976.
[368] Shearer, Lloyd, "Charlie Bossart, Father of the Atlas," *Parade*, March 1, 1959.
[369] Blair, Clay Jr., "Passing of a Great Mind", *Life*, February 25, 1957.

Deterrence was put to the test in 1962, when the Cuban missile crisis brought Russia and the United States into a dangerous confrontation. During that summer and fall, the Soviet Union installed five nuclear-missile regiments, amounting to forty R-12 and R-14 missiles.[370] These were medium-range rockets that could strike the United States from Cuba. They were discovered by U-2 photo-reconnaissance planes early in October, and on the 22nd, President Kennedy publicly denounced them.

At that time, the U.S.A. had 203 ICBMs deployed, including 129 Atlas missiles. That was the maximum number of Atlas missiles deployed before they were decommissioned for military use in 1965. By 1962, America was already beginning to replace the Atlas ICBM with the solid-fuel Minuteman missiles. The Soviet Union had 36 ICBMs in 1962, including four of the old R-7 rockets. Only a few of the gigantic and expensive R-7s were ever deployed as weapons. The backbone of the Russian missile fleet was the R-16, half the size and carrying a 3000-pound warhead.

The situation with the Cuban missiles was volatile, and a mistake could have been disastrous. On October 24, in the middle of the crisis, Sergei Korolev's team attempted to launch a space probe to Mars. But when it began its interplanetary trajectory burn, the orbiting rocket stage exploded over Africa. Passing over Alaska, two-dozen pieces of debris were detected by the early warning radar, triggering an alert. Fortunately, it was identified as a false alarm before any drastic action was taken.

Eventually the missile crisis was resolved. Russia withdrew its rockets from Cuba, and America secretly agreed to remove its missiles from Turkey. Medium-range missiles, on the borders of the USA or USSR, could strike almost without warning, giving little chance to retaliate. However, that made the strategic situation unstable in a way that the ICBM did not. They created an incentive to strike preemptively before the opponent reaches the same decision. The dire prospect of a push-button nuclear war, which would have wiped out both sides, forced the two super powers to react thoughtfully and negotiate a peaceful solution to the conflict.

---

[370] Sherwin, Martin J., "The Cuban Missile Crisis at 50: In Search of Historical Perspective," *Prologue Magazine*, Vol. 44, No. 2 (National Archives).

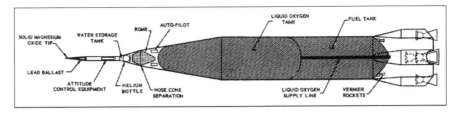

Diagram of five-engine MX-1593 missile from 1953 (*Courtesy of Bossart Family*).

Stages in manufacture of the Atlas: unrolling stainless steel sheet metal, sheets fashioned into body segment rings, completed rocket hulls assembled from segments (*Courtesy of San Diego Air and Space Museum*).

Atlas launch (*U.S. Air Force*).

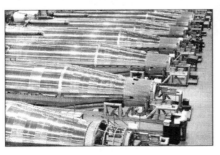

6

Space Rocket

The Atlas and the R-7 were the world's first ICBMs, but they both ended up serving as space rockets and continued to do so long after they were retired as weapons. For military deployment and rapid response, liquid fuel rockets (especially using super-cold liquid oxygen) took too much time to prepare for launch. Eventually, solid-fuel ICBMs such as Minuteman and the Soviet RT-2 took their place, able to be launched on a moment's notice. But the more powerful and efficient liquid-fuel rockets remained essential for space exploration, where performance had to be much higher than for surface-to-surface ballistic flight.

Charlie had developed an interest in space travel after the war. He was on von Braun's 1952 satellite committee, was elected a Fellow of the American Rocket Society in 1954, and he co-authored one of the early documents that called for the creation of NASA. In a 1957 interview, he made his views clear: "Forget about the military applications of rockets for a minute, and think of all the peaceful applications: shooting mail from coast to coast by rocket, manned travel to Mars, interplanetary communications, better weather forecasting, detailed aerial maps."[371]

On January 31, 1958, the Army launched the first American satellite, using a rocket that had been ready for more than a year. The Juno missile, built by von Braun, was an enlarged Redstone topped by extra stages of the Army's solid-fuel Sergeant missiles. It was not an elegant design, but it got Explorer-1 into orbit. Onboard the satellite, James Van Allen's Geiger

---

[371] Shearer, Lloyd, "Charlie Bossart, Father of the Atlas," *Parade*, March 1, 1959.

counter detected the existence of radiation belts around the Earth, the first major scientific discovery of the space age.

On May 15, the one-and-a-half-ton Sputnik-3 entered orbit. Called an "automatic physics laboratory," it contained 12 experiments to study cosmic radiation, electromagnetic fields, micrometeorites and the upper atmosphere. It was a surprisingly sophisticated satellite, and the small Juno and Vanguard rockets were nowhere near capable of launching anything of comparable weight and complexity. Premier Khrushchev joked that the U.S.A. would have to launch many satellites the size of an orange to catch up with the Soviet Union (referring to the tiny Vanguard satellite). A month later, Charlie told members of the American Rocket Society that the Atlas could put a satellite of equal size to Sputnik-3 into orbit if it used a second stage. "Unfortunately, we only move when Uncle Sam says 'go.'"[372]

Charlie had hired one of the most imaginative proponents of space exploration. Krafft Ehricke had done research at Peenemünde, under Walter Thiel, the man who developed the V-2 engine. After the war, he worked for the U.S. Army at Huntsville, but he grew dissatisfied by von Braun's conservative style. He was particularly interested in developing liquid hydrogen as a rocket fuel, and von Braun was disdainful of the idea. Charlie tried to hire him in 1951, but Ehricke's security clearance was not yet high enough to work on the Atlas project.[373] Instead, Ehricke went to work for the former head of the V-2 project, Walter Dornberger, at Bell Aircraft. In November of 1954, Ehricke was in California, for a job interview at Aerojet.

He stopped by Convair to visit Charlie, who asked if he had made a firm promise to Aerojet. When told no, he said, "By golly, you're fair game and I'm going to offer you a job!" Ehricke was one of a small number of co-workers with whom Charlie and his family socialized. Ehricke later said, "Charlie is a wonderful guy. I just adore the guy."

Ehricke calculated that the five-engine Atlas design could reach orbit with a useful payload. But when the missile was downsized to fit the smallest possible warhead, Ehricke called it a "self-defeating efficiency." The first design of the three-engine Atlas was not capable of reaching space, but with later improvements, he showed Charlie that the Atlas could reach orbit, even without the addition of a second stage.[374] But just barely. General Schriever did not want any time and resources going into space travel, and he made it clear that getting the Atlas to work as quickly as

---

[372] AP Wire, June 10, 1958.
[373] Chapman, John L., *Atlas: The Story of a Missile*, Harper, New York, 1960.
[374] Interview of Dr. Krafft Ehricke, John L. Sloop, NASA, 1974.

possible was a national priority, "I don't want to catch anybody thinking anything but Atlas." But with regard to Ehricke's ideas about spaceflight, Charlie told him in private, "We'll not completely neglect this."

In the summer of 1958, Charlie gave a talk on the problem of interplanetary space travel in St. Louis at a meeting of the Institute of Aeronautical Sciences.[375] The problem of flying to another planet had been considered by Tsiolkovsky in 1903, who advocated an elliptical path between two planets. The same idea was proposed again in the 1920s by a German named Hohmann, but their work only solved a toy version of the problem. Set in two dimensions, it considered only the gravity of the Sun, and treated the planets as simple points of departure and arrival.

Charlie analyzed a more complex and realistic problem in three dimensions, starting and ending on the surface of the Earth and including the effect of planetary gravity. He calculated the energy needed for direct launch from the surface or launching from orbit, and he considered different strategies for returning to Earth, such as air braking, or rendezvous with an orbiting station. Considerably more weight could be sent to another planet by first going into orbit and then performing a second rocket burn to fling the spacecraft like a sling shot.

In the months following Sputnik, the Space Flight Committee of the American Rocket Society prepared a report for President Eisenhower, advocating the formation of a national space agency and suggesting a number of research projects: satellites, space stations, missions to the Moon and planets. The committee included the three foremost rocket designers working for the Army, Navy and Air Force: Wernher von Braun, Milton Rosen, and Charlie Bossart.[376]

In March of 1958, the President drafted a bill to create the National Aeronautics and Space Administration (NASA), and Congress enacted the law in July. It consolidated parts of the three competing military rocket programs, as well as the NACA, which had overseen aircraft research since 1915.

Before the Atlas rocket reached its potential as a space vehicle, the late 1950s was a frustrating period for NASA. Several attempts were made to launch lunar probes using the Juno II rockets built by von Braun. These small missiles were able to launch only tiny payloads. They could not

---

[375] Bossart, Karel J., "Departure and Return in Interplanetary Flight," *Aero/Space Engineering*, October, 1958. The talk was presented on May 14.

[376] *New York* Times, December 5, 1957.; Space Flight Technical Committee of the American Rocket Society, "A National Space Flight Program," *Astronautics* 3 (Jan. 1958).; Charlie Bossart became a Fellow of the ARS in 1954.

support sophisticated upper stages with guidance systems, so these early Pioneer probes missed the Moon by tens of thousands of miles.

By 1958, after Sputnik-3, the administration was tired of being embarrassed by Russia's massive rocket. On a visit to Convair, an Air Force research representative complained, "We've got to get something big up." He was surprised when Dempsey told him, "Well, we can put the whole Atlas in orbit." Charlie, Ehricke and Dempsey were called to Washington to discuss the idea, but the Air Force demanded the achievement of a full 5500-mile ICBM test flight before they would let any time be spent on a satellite. But privately, President Eisenhower liked the Atlas satellite idea and authorized a secret initiative to make it happen.

When the first Sputnik was launched in 1957, the public got the impression that President Eisenhower was befuddled by what had happened. But in fact since early 1956, he had been involved in planning a highly classified system of military satellites to detect missile launches and photograph enemy territory. The CIA and Lockheed Aircraft were busy developing the KH-1, America's first reconnaissance satellite. But in his public press interviews, Eisenhower never gave the slightest indication that he had thought about satellites.

For the Atlas satellite mission, the President did not want a repeat of the embarrassing Vanguard mission, where public expectations were disappointed by a spectacular failure. In 1958, when Atlas 10B was allocated to this project, only 88 people in the world knew it was slated to go into orbit. The cover story was that it was being stripped down for a super-long-range test flight to the Indian Ocean. The project, named SCORE (Signal Communication by Orbiting Relay Equipment) was so secret that even the originators of the idea, Krafft Ehricke and Charlie Bossart, were not told. With word coming down from the President and Curtis LeMay, General Schriever made it clear that he meant business about secrecy; if one of the civilians leaked the mission, they would lose their security clearance and "spend the rest of their lives selling cars or shoes."

10B was discreetly modified in several ways. It was one of the lighter "hotrod" versions of the B series, and even more weight was removed to create what they called a "super strip" configuration.[377] A hollow aerodynamic nose cone replaced the heavy reentry vehicle, and a new engine with slightly higher exhaust speed was installed. At the last minute a number of unneeded systems were stripped out to save weight, including the nose cone separation system and the Azusa tracking transponder.

---

[377] Davis, Deane, "The Talking Satellite: A Reminiscence of Project SCORE," *JBIS*, 1999.

Instruments in the side nacelles were mounted in standardized cylindrical canisters, and it was relatively easy to remove or swap in new devices. A pair of radio units were installed, each consisting of an eight-watt vacuum-tube transmitter, a transistorized receiver, a four-minute tape recorder and a silver-zinc battery.[378]

On December 18, 1958, many of the blockhouse technicians at launch complex LC-11 still did not know that the rocket was going to attempt orbit. As usual, Charlie was at the Cape to observe the test. He could sense that something was up, and he cornered Dempsey and asked if 10B was going into orbit. Dempsey said he could not talk about it, which essentially answered Charlie's question. As the countdown proceeded, the Azusa station reported no transponder signal. The Azusa system was one of the redundant tracking systems used to ensure that the missile did not go off course, but to everyone's surprise, the Chief of Range Safety did not hold the countdown.

The rocket lifted off at 6:02 pm. Fueled to burn an extra 13 seconds, the rocket accelerated to 17,000 miles per hour. In Central Control, the true nature of the mission dawned on everyone as they watched the impact-prediction plotter go beyond the landing zone and literally off the chart. The rocket entered an eccentric elliptical orbit with a period of 101.47 minutes, ranging from 115 to 922 miles in altitude.[379]

The Army Signal Corps, who built the onboard radio system, organized five ground stations across the southern United States, forming a fence that the satellite's orbit would frequently cross. On its first orbit, when it passed over the tracking station in California, the primary radio unit did not work. The next day, the back-up radio was activated. During a mid-afternoon pass over Cape Canaveral, it was commanded to transmit a prerecorded message from President Eisenhower:

This is the President of the United States speaking. Through the marvels of scientific advance, my voice is coming to you from a satellite traveling in outer space. My message is a simple one: Through this unique means I convey to you and all mankind, America's wish for peace on Earth and goodwill toward men everywhere.

SCORE was the world's first communications satellite. The radio batteries had an eight-hour capacity, so the system was used sparingly to perform experiments over the next two weeks. Besides the prerecorded message, the

---

[378] Brown, S.P. and G.F. Senn, "Project SCORE," *Proc. IRE*, April 1960.
[379] Formally named "Zeta 1958," orbital elements given in RAE Table of Earth Satellites, 1958.

satellite was able to record new messages or relay voice in real time from one ground station to another. In the following days after the launch, the President's speech was replaced with test messages, and ham radio enthusiasts would hear messages such as, "This is Prado Dam, United States Army Signal Research and Development Laboratory, Corona, California…" The system was controlled by transmitting audio tones to the satellite, which sometimes happened by accident. While passing over New England, a radio station activated the recorder and uploaded several minutes of swing-band music, much to the surprise of the ground stations the next time it passed over.[380] In all, 78 radio-communication experiments were performed on 28 uploaded messages, and 43 minutes of real-time relayed speech between ground stations.

The large stainless steel rocket was as bright as a planet. With an orbital inclination of 32.3°, it was visible over South Africa, and Dora and her husband lay on their backs in the garden to watch the bright satellite. She sent her brother a telegram: CONGRATULATIONS SPLENDID ACHIEVEMENT SAW ATLAS RIGHT ABOVE OUR HEADS.[381] When Charlie read the cable, he smiled and told his family, "I knew all the time the Atlas would work."

American newspapers were proud to point out that the four ton satellite was three times the weight of Sputnik-3.[382] It was a triumph for the United States and for President Eisenhower, who had been criticized for his weak responses to Soviet rocketry. The transmitter ran out of battery power 12 days later, and the low-orbiting missile reentered the atmosphere on January 21, burning up over Midway Island in the Pacific.

Not everyone was thrilled by the SCORE experiment.[383] Wernher von Braun and his colleagues at Huntsville said little about the project, which promoted their "inflated competition" (as they derisively referred to the pressure-stabilized Atlas). A few years later, when he published his famous book, *History of Rocketry and Space Travel*, von Braun spent pages talking about Milton Rosen and his ill-fated Vanguard rocket. By failing so dramatically, the Vanguard was a nonthreatening alternative to his own rockets. But he never mentioned Bossart and spent only one sentence about the Atlas design, "a thin pressurized airframe, which was not ideal for advanced, higher-acceleration takeoffs".[384] In fact, the take-off acceleration of Atlas was almost twice that of Titan.

---

[380] Walker, Chuck, *Atlas: The Ultimate Weapon*, Apogee, 2005.
[381] Western Union telegram from South Africa, December 22, 1958, courtesy of Jan Bossart.
[382] Strictly speaking, including the R-7 sustainer stage, the Soviets orbited nine tons. The Russians complained, but at that time, they were not willing to disclose the weight of their rocket stage.
[383] Dickson, Paul, *Sputnik: The Shock of the Century*, G.K.Hall, 2001.

The Atlas B could boost only a small payload into orbit. The next step to use the missile for space exploration was to add a second stage. When interviewed after the launch of the SCORE satellite, Charlie told reporters, "With something else on top of it, the Atlas can reach the Moon or Venus."[385] He was referring to a specific project, an Air Force plan to send a space probe to Venus, using the Able upper stage. [386]

Able was a two-ton rocket stage built by Douglas Aircraft and powered by an Aerojet engine. It was more or less the second stage of the Vanguard rocket, and it had an ancestry going back to the Army's WAC Corporal missile. All these rockets were powered by room-temperature liquid propellants: nitric acid and dimethyl hydrazine. These chemicals combusted on contact, which provided a completely trustworthy engine ignition. The Atlas team had avoided a design with upper stages because of their experience with unreliable pyrotechnic engine starting. In a later version (model D) of Atlas, the engines started with the same kind of chemical ignition, before switching over to LOX and kerosene. This technique finally laid to rest the problem that had plagued Charlie's team since MX-774.

Venus and Earth would align for a transfer trajectory in June of 1959, and a probe was designed with a dozen scientific experiments, a radio system, four paddle-wheel solar panels, and a retro engine to slow it down enough to enter orbit around the planet. But the U.S. did not yet have the technology to send a probe to Venus. The lack of an interplanetary radio system meant they could not send instructions to make course corrections or receive any telemetry data from the other planet. Consequently, the plans were changed to simplify the probes and put them into Lunar orbit.

The Air Force married the Able stage to their Thor medium-range missile, and heavier scientific probes were designed for Atlas/Able vehicles. Unfortunately, the program was plagued by bad luck. In 1958, all three of the Thor/Able missions failed. The next year, four attempts were made with an Able stage mounted on an Atlas but none of them were successful.

On September 9, 1959, the Atlas 9C with an Able upper stage was undergoing a routine static test at the Cape. About five seconds into the test, some bubbles were sucked into the LOX turbo pump, it revved too fast and the engine automatically shut down. A water-hammer shock broke the plumbing and liquid oxygen began leaking and feeding a fire in the tail section.

---

[384] Von Braun, Wernher and Frederick Ordway, *History of Rocketry and Space Travel*, Crowell, 1966.
[385] Rogers, Warren Jr. "Device Circling Earth nearly 3 Times Sputnik III's Weight," Associated Press, December 19, 1958.
[386] *A Development Plan for Two Interplanetary Probes (ABLE-4)*, STL Report, January 14, 1959.

The Atlas was filled with 19,000 gallons of liquid oxygen and 12,000 gallons of kerosene. Half a minute after the engines were shut down, the Atlas collapsed and exploded violently. A fireball enveloped the pad and the surrounding area. Inside the bunker, the launch crew were trapped for hours, before it was safe to go outside and survey the damage. It took seven months to rebuild the launch complex LC-12.

Three Atlas/Able missions were launched from the Cape. In November, the fiberglass payload fairing broke off, 45 seconds after take-off. The aerodynamic load ripped the probe off the rocket, but the Atlas and Able stages still performed correctly. In September of 1960, the Atlas performed normally, but the Able stage malfunctioned and dumped the lunar probe into the Indian Ocean. That December, a final attempt was made, but the Able stage ignited during the flight and its engine destroyed the Atlas.

The Soviet Union, with its giant R-7 rocket, continued to surprise the West with space accomplishments. In 1959, they developed a third stage for the rocket and used it to impact the Moon (Luna-2) and take the first photographs of the far side (Luna-3). This "E" stage, as they called it, was big enough to contain a complete guidance system, so the Russians were able to achieve an accuracy of a few hundred miles at lunar distances. After the embarrassment of not detecting the "Van Allen" radiation belts, the Luna probes allowed Soviet scientists to make their first major scientific discovery: the solar wind.

Charlie had pointed out the advantages of launching space probes from orbit, rather than going directly from the launch pad into deep space, as the Atlas/Able and Juno II attempted to do. Soviet scientists reached the same conclusion, and Korolev completed a version of the R-7 that put a fourth stage into orbit. After circling the earth, the new "L" stage was able to orient itself and fire its engine. In October of 1960, the Russians attempted to launch two probes with cameras to the planet Mars. But both Mars rockets failed to reach orbit.

The next February, they succeeded in sending the first interplanetary probe toward Venus. The 1400-pound Venera-1 returned new data about micrometeorites and cosmic rays far outside the influence of the Earth's magnetosphere. Like modern space probes, it was able to orient itself to the stars and aim a dish antenna to the Earth and perform mid-course corrections with an onboard rocket engine. However, after a telemetry session from more than a million miles away (only a few percent of the way to Venus), Venera-1 went silent, its orientation sensors destroyed by the heat of the Sun.[387]

Long before the Soviets demonstrated their orbital "L" stage, American experts knew that the Atlas needed an oriented orbiting second stage. Early in 1959 the Naval Research Lab commissioned Convair to build the Vega stage. They proposed a short unit built from Atlas tank components, with just the hemispherical end caps and one cylindrical section. Using the LOX/kerosene engine from the Vanguard first stage, it would have been a collaboration between Charlie's team and Milton Rosen's Vanguard team. It would increase the Atlas payload capacity to 5800 pounds into orbit, or 1300 pounds for an interplanetary probe launched from orbit. Convair agreed to work on Vega, somewhat reluctantly.[388] However, the project was cancelled at the end of the year.

The first technology that allowed Atlas to properly launch space probes was the Agena stage. Built by Lockheed, it was part of Eisenhower's military reconnaissance satellite program that began in 1956. It was originally planned for the Agena to be the platform for the spy satellite, providing it with orientation and aiming capability. It was also used simply as an oriented rocket stage.

Since 1959, the Air Force had been using Agena, mounted on its medium-range Thor missile, to orbit KH ("Key Hole") reconnaissance satellites. Starting with the two-ton KH-7 Gambit satellite, they began to use the more powerful Atlas/Agena combination. The empty Gambit weighed 1000 pounds and carried 3000 feet of film that it could expose and drop to Earth.[389]

The first KH-7 met an ignominious end. The Atlas was famous for its pressure-stabilized airframe. Pressurization never failed during flight, but there were a few mishaps on the launch pad. In 1959, Atlas 1D was punctured by a falling tool and collapsed before it could be tested. On May 11, 1963, Atlas 190D was being prepared to launch the first KH-7 from Vandenberg Air Force Base. During the loading of the liquid oxygen, the plumbing was damaged and it was decided to drain it. Just as the tank was empty, there was a loss of pressurization. The top of the rocket buckled under the weight of the Agena, and the Gambit fell off, dashing the massive telescopic camera to the ground. The hull continued to unravel,

[387] Mitchell, Don P., *The Soviet Exploration of Venus*, www.mentallandscape.com, 2003.
[388] "Interview of Dr. Krafft Ehricke by John L. Sloop," NASA, 1974.
[389] Outzen, James, *Critical to US Security: The Gambit and Hexagon Satellite Reconnaissance Systems*, Center for the Study of National Reconnaissance, 2012.

disintegrating from the top down and splashing its load of kerosene over the launch pad. Fortunately, nothing started it on fire.[390]

The first space missions for Atlas/Agena were the Ranger probes, sent to study the Moon at close range with cameras and sensors. Like the ill-fated Pioneer-Able missions, the Ranger program was fraught with difficulty. The first six Rangers failed, due to Agena or spacecraft malfunctions, leading to congressional hearings and shakeups in NASA's management. Khrushchev again teased NASA, saying that the Luna-2 probe was getting lonesome on the surface of the Moon, waiting for an American companion. Finally in July 1964, Ranger-7 was successful and sent back the closest and most detailed images ever seen of the lunar surface. After that success, Atlas-Agena rockets launched the Lunar Orbiter missions, which generated the first detailed maps of the entire Moon, including the far side that had been seen only in fuzzy Soviet images.

Ironically, an American spacecraft visited the planet Venus two years before the country had a successful Moon probe. On August 27, 1962, a repurposed Ranger spacecraft named Mariner-2 was launched to Venus by Atlas 179D.

Radio telescopes had detected microwave signals from Venus, indicating temperatures as high as 620° F, but there was a controversy over whether this indicated a hot ionosphere or a hot surface. As it approached Venus, the Sun heated the spacecraft to 200° F and many of its systems failed, but it was still able to complete its mission. Scanning the planet at close range, it found the heat signature was weaker at the edges, which indicated that the surface rather than the upper atmosphere was hot. It was the end of the idea that Venus might be a lush tropical world teaming with life.

The world's first successful Mars mission was Mariner-4, sent in November 1964 by Atlas 288D. Pictures sent back from Mars profoundly changed our ideas about the planet, revealing a crater-pocked Moon-like landscape. As with Venus, the popular fantasy of Mars as an inhabited world, with canals and cities came to an end.

Agena was not originally intended to be the Atlas upper stage for planetary launches. Not long after work began on the spy satellite program that resulted in Agena, a powerful space-mission stage for the Atlas was planned, called Centaur. It was designed to put 8400 pounds into orbit, or

[390] Perry, Robert L., *A History of Satellite Reconnaissance*, Department of Defense, 1973 (declassified 2011).

send 2610 pounds on an interplanetary trajectory. But delays in the Centaur project meant that Agena had to be pressed into service.

The idea for Centaur was born at Convair, where Krafft Ehricke had been promoted to head of the Preliminary Design Department. In 1956, he and his engineering staff prepared some plans for a liquid hydrogen/liquid oxygen stage, as part of a number of space-exploration projects.

Dempsey dropped by one day and saw the plans, asking "What the hell is that?" When Ehricke explained the idea, Dempsey told him, "Well Krafft, you know you're kind of a nut anyway. Go ahead, do it…Don't spend too much money." Mort Rosenbaum, Chief Engineer at Convair Astronautics, thought the idea was nonsense and a waste of time, but Charlie and Dempsey foresaw the future importance of space rockets and realized that Atlas would have a limited lifetime as an ICBM.[391]

As Technical Director, Charlie encouraged Ehricke's Centaur work and was part of the initial design team. Convair practiced matrix management, where two different chains of management overlapped. The management system was an adaptation to the necessity of juggling multiple military contracts. Program managers oversaw individual projects, which came and went over time. Department management was a stable long-term structure, in charge of divisions such as engineering, reliability control, product support, etc. Ehricke was the Centaur program director, and Rosenbaum was the division chief of engineering. In his position, Charlie had the authority to tell Ehricke or Rosenbaum to change anything if he did not like it, but in general he let creative people run their own show.[392]

Liquid hydrogen and liquid oxygen as propellants were first proposed by Tsiolkovsky in 1903, just a few years after the liquefaction of hydrogen was first accomplished. Charlie had considered hydrogen for the MX-774, when he was hoping to build a single-stage ICBM. Hydrogen has the highest chemical energy per pound of any liquid fuel. While kerosene/LOX could produce an exhaust velocity of 11,500 ft/sec in an efficient engine, LOX/LH2 could achieve 14,500 ft/sec.

At 423° F below zero, liquid hydrogen was very difficult to produce and handle. By 1956, only 500 pounds of LH2 was produced in the entire United States. However, the Air Force developed industrial-scale hydrogen liquefaction facilities to support an experimental aircraft project, and Pratt & Whitney had developed a 15,000-pound rocket engine (the RL-10) for

[391] Interview of Dr. Krafft Ehricke by John L. Sloop, NASA, 1974.
[392] Interview of Mr. K.J. Bossart by John L. Sloop, NASA, 1974.; Ames, Charles S., "The Atlas Program at General Dynamics/Astronautics," *Science, Technology, and Management*, 1963.

that project. The aircraft project was cancelled, but two of the engines powered the Centaur.

Centaur's structure was based on the structural philosophy of Atlas—a thin pressure-stabilized stainless steel tank. Liquid hydrogen had a very low density, so the fuel tank had to be very large. Thus Charlie's pressurized-steel-balloon concept was eminently suited to liquid hydrogen. One quirk of liquid hydrogen was that its tiny molecules could leak out through any microscopic cracks, and the process used to build Atlas had to be modified and combined with more extensive inspections.[393]

Liquid hydrogen was so cold that it required some insulation, and fiberglass panels covered the outside of the LH2 tank, jettisoned at 50 miles altitude once air friction became negligible. In the Atlas, Charlie found that kerosene and liquid oxygen could coexist in tanks separated only by a thin bulkhead of stainless steel. But LH2 would freeze liquid oxygen and boil from the heat it absorbed in so doing. In Centaur, this problem was solved by two closely spaced bulkheads separating the propellants, and the space between the bulkheads was filled with nitrogen gas. The nitrogen was frozen by the liquid hydrogen, creating a vacuum thermal barrier between the two tanks. The idea for making a "cryo-vacuum" was first worked out by Ehricke and friends drawing on the table-cloth at a restaurant.

Convair prepared an Atlas/Centaur presentation using a scale model of the two-stage rocket. Charlie would talk first on how the Atlas worked, detaching the booster and tail section, and then the Centaur stage. At that point, Ehricke would describe the functions of the second stage. They decided to make a film of the presentation but when Charlie tried to pull the Centaur stage off the Atlas model, it would not budge. As he struggled, people started to laugh. He realized someone had glued them together as a joke, and he quickly joined in the laughter.[394]

Centaur started out as an Air Force project, but shortly after the creation of NASA, it became a civilian project under the space agency's control. In June of 1960, the Army missile group at Huntsville, run by Wernher von Braun, became part of NASA. It was named the Marshall Space Flight Center, and it was immediately tasked with project management of Centaur. Von Braun was not a fan of hydrogen as a propellant or of Centaur and Atlas. They competed with his plan for NASA to use the Saturn rockets, combined with the Agena upper stage. Despite von Braun's misgivings about the project, he appointed a good engineer to

---

[393] Interview of Mr. K.J. Bossart by John L. Sloop, NASA, 1974.; *Centaur Technical Handbook*, General Dynamics Report GD/A-BPM64, October 1, 1964.

[394] Martin, Richard E., "The Atlas and Centaur "Steel Balloon" Tanks: A Legacy of Karel Bossart," *AAS History Series, Vol 17*, AAS, San Diego, 1995.

oversee it. Hans Hueter got along well with the Convair team. He and Ehricke had been friends at Peenemünde, and Charlie liked him too.

Usually gregarious and comfortable with people from all walks of life, Charlie was ill at ease with Wernher von Braun and some of his engineers. The problem was not the history of conflict between Belgium and Germany; but rather, his disagreement with von Braun's design and management philosophy. The German rocket designer represented many of the things that had led Charlie to leave Europe and embrace American culture. The Convair team viewed Huntsville as too conservative and authoritarian, while von Braun saw the Centaur team as unruly.[395] Von Braun never believed in Charlie's stainless-steel-balloon designs, and Charlie thought von Braun's rockets were heavy conservative structures, "built like the Brooklyn Bridge."[396]

The next year, von Braun decided to get better acquainted with the Centaur-development team at Convair. He flew to San Diego, bringing an entourage of his top engineers. There was concern that the two master engineers might get into a bitter argument about structural design, but Charlie promised "I'll wear my shiny new halo." During the tour, Charlie showed them around the Sycamore Canyon test site and the Atlas plant, and he let Ehricke answer questions about the Centaur stage.

However, trouble began in the afternoon session. At a long presentation in the conference room, Charlie was seated next to Willie Mrazek,[397] a Peenemünde veteran and von Braun's chief of structures. As the meeting progressed, the two of them began a private conversation, whispering and gesturing, clearly having a disagreement.[398] When it became clear they were disrupting the presentation and getting looks from von Braun and Dempsey, the two engineers stepped outside. A few others followed them to hear the debate.

Once outside, Charlie led everyone to a discarded Atlas tank, which was used for testing. He asked someone to fetch his hammer, and everyone except Mrazek knew what was coming: Charlie's beloved hit-the-tank test. An Atlas had once been destroyed when a worker dropped a sharp tool that punctured a tank, so to avoid damaging an expensive missile, Charlie had been presented with a special seven-pound rubber-coated lead mallet just for this purpose.

[395] Dawson & Bowles, *Taming Liquid Hydrogen: The Centaur Upper Stage Rocket*, NASA, 2004.
[396] "Interview of Mr. K.J. Bossart by John L. Sloop," NASA, 1974.
[397] William Anthony Mrazek (1911-1992).
[398] Davis, Deane, "Seeing is Believing, or, How the Atlas Rocket Hit Back," *Spaceflight*, 1983.; Sloop, John L., *Visit to Convair Aerospace Division, General Dynamics*, NASA, April 29, 1974 (contains Charlie's telling of the Mrazek incident).

The tank, only 3 hundredths of an inch thick, was kept at its standby pressure of 9 pounds per square inch, a quarter of the flight pressure. Even when empty, the Atlas tanks would cave in without internal pressurization. Mrazek asked about the internal structural support framework, and Charlie told him there was nothing but nitrogen inside. Charlie handed the hammer to the Austrian engineer.

"Whack it!"

Mrazek gave it a tap and checked to see if the metal was dented.

"No, Willie, belt it!"

He hit it harder, and Charlie urged, "Willie, stop fiddling around. Hit the damned thing!"

This time Mrazek gave it a strong blow, and the hammer bounced off the stiff metal surface and flew out of his grip, knocking his glasses off and landing 15 feet away. Muttering German curses under his breath, he inspected the tank and still could not find any sign of a dent. Seeing Mrazek pick up the hammer again, Bossart's staff decided to end the game before someone got clobbered. They whisked Mrazek back to the meeting. Satisfied with the outcome, Charlie strolled back inside, whistling a tune.

The first launch of Atlas/Centaur was May 8, 1962. Unfortunately, the insulating shroud on the Centaur broke loose, and the overheated hydrogen boiled in the tank and burst it open, causing the rocket to explode. A Congressional hearing quickly followed, and von Braun advised them to cancel the Centaur project. NASA management was infuriated by von Braun's statements, and the management of Centaur was transferred to the Lewis Research Center, where much of the pioneering research in hydrogen propulsion was first done.[399] The next year, the second test was a success. After a number of experimental launches, it began real work in 1966.

The first success of the Atlas/Centaur rocket was project Surveyor, America's first probes to land on the Moon and return television images of the surface. All seven of those missions were launched successfully, and five of them completed their missions (two crashed on the Moon, through no fault of the Atlas/Centaur). The missions paved the way for the Apollo landings on the Moon.

Atlas/Centaur carried the Mariner 6 and 7 flybys of Mars, the Mariner-9 Mars orbiter and two Viking Mars landers. It also launched the Mariner-10 flybys of Venus and Mercury, and the Pioneer and Voyager missions to the outer gas-giant planets. The Pioneer-Venus probes entered the atmosphere and went into orbit around the cloud-covered planet. At the

---

[399] Sloop, John L., *Liquid Hydrogen as a Propulsion Fuel, 1945-1959*, NASA, 1978.

same time, the Atlas fuel capacity was increased by adding more cylindrical segments to its propellant tank. The rocket was used to launch a number of geosynchronous satellites and secret military payloads. In all, 148 Atlas Centaur missions were launched.

The Atlas also played an important part in manned missions. On the evening of November 18, 1959, the American Rocket Society held its annual honors dinner in Washington D.C. Charlie was presented with the James H. Wyld Memorial Award, named after the man who designed the rocket engines for Reaction Motors Inc. One of his engines powered the MX-774 test missile.

Following the ceremony, reporters interviewed Charlie. After 10 successful launches in a row, he believed that the Atlas rocket had achieved the reliability necessary for manned flight. It could be used immediately, he said, to put a man into orbit, if only a space capsule were available.

The manned space program was underway at the same time as the Agena and Centaur projects. The first serious study of the problem was initiated by the Air Force in 1956. In April of 1958, they issued a four-part proposal. The first part was called "Man in Space Soonest," short missions to put monkeys and then humans briefly into orbit. Next would be orbital missions lasting many days, then unmanned probes on the Moon, and finally a manned mission to the Moon. With the formation of NASA, the first part of this plan became Project Mercury. [400]

Eleven aircraft companies responded with designs for manned space capsules. Three of them planned to use Atlas/Agena as the launch vehicle. Two proposed using Atlas combined with the Navy's Polaris missile as a second stage. Convair submitted plans for a 1000-pound space capsule five feet in diameter, to be launched by an Atlas/Agena. Like the MX-774 warhead, their reentry capsule was spherical. Convair also proposed larger spacecraft and space stations based on empty Atlas tanks, assembled together in orbit.

Convair's capsule design was not selected, but their Atlas rocket would be the launch vehicle for Project Mercury. McDonnell Aircraft Corporation was chosen to design the Mercury capsule. It could be mounted either on von Braun's Redstone rocket for the early ballistic test flights, or on the Atlas for orbital missions. By this time, the orbital payload capacity of the Atlas had increased substantially since the SCORE mission.

On September 9, 1959, the Atlas 10D launched the "Big Joe" mission, to test an empty Mercury capsule and its heat shield. Although the rocket

[400] Grimwood, James M., *Project Mercury: A Chronology*, NASA, 1963.

failed to drop the booster stage, the mission was mostly successful. Thirteen minutes after launch, the capsule dropped into the Atlantic 1500 miles from the Cape, and was retrieved for study.

Charlie flew out to the Cape for the Mercury flights. In 1960, the Starlite Motel was sold, and the new owner clamped down on the rowdy behavior and off-color decorations. Henri Landwirth decided to quit and take a job at the nearby Holiday Inn. The astronauts and Convair engineers followed him, and the Inn replaced the Starlite as the new social center of the rocketry elite.[401]

The next unmanned test flight, Atlas 50D, started out fine. At 9:13 EST, on July 29 of 1960, the rocket took off and disappeared into low cloud cover. But 58 second after launch, all the radio signals from the missile disappeared. Just one seconds of telemetry data before the failure indicated a loss of tank pressure, and signals from the Mercury capsule indicated violent motions. The rocket came down in pieces about seven miles from shore, and NASA began searching the shallow waters for clues in the debris.[402]

For the first time, the stainless-steel-balloon airframe had failed during flight. At a meeting two months later, the Air Force and Convair suggested that the Mercury capsule broke up and pieces struck the sides of the Atlas. But the failure occurred just as the rocket was breaking the speed of sound. At transonic speed, aircraft experience strong disturbances as shock waves form and shift position. So it was concluded that air moving past the Mercury capsule generated buffeting that caused the thin skin of the Atlas to ripple and buckle.[403]

Convair strengthened the design of the hull in that area, but before those new versions would be coming off the assembly line, NASA decided to modify the rockets it already owned. They added an 8-inch band of stainless steel at the top of the rocket, doubling its thickness. The Air Force was unhappy about this and worried that NASA did not know how to operate the Atlas and might generate bad publicity for their missile by wrecking a number of them. Fortunately, with the reinforcing "horse collar" as some called it, the next Mercury-Atlas sub-orbital test was completely successful, and the capsule splashed down 1432 miles from the Cape.

[401] Charlie's letters home were written on Holiday Inn stationery.
[402] Swenson, Grimwood & Alexander, *This New Ocean: A History of Project Mercury*, NASA, 1966.
[403] Swanson, Glen E., *"Before This Decade Is Out...,"* NASA, 1999.; Martin, Richard E., "The Atlas and Centaur "Steel Balloon" Tanks: A Legacy of Karel Bossart," *AAS History Series, Vol 17*, AAS, San Diego, 1995.

Von Braun's Redstone missile had its problems as well. The first Mercury-Redstone test rose only slightly before the engines shut down and the parachutes popped out of the capsule. It was derided as a "four-inch flight." On January 31, 1961, the MR-2 missions successfully propelled a chimpanzee named Ham to a distance of 422 miles.

On April 12, 1961, hopes were dashed for America to be first with a man in space. A young Russian pilot named Yuri Gagarin lifted off from Baikonur, calling out over the radio, "*Poyekhali!*" (Let's go!). The Vostok-1 space craft was launched by a three-stage rocket, similar to the one used for lunar missions, and it made one orbit. Like Convair's Mercury capsule proposal, the Vostok was spherical.

In the Soviet Union, there was not a strong separation of the civilian and military space programs. The Vostok manned capsule was the same vehicle as the *Zenit* spy satellite, which would carry a 2000-mm camera instead of a cosmonaut. Zenit had a sophisticated orientation system, so it could aim its cameras accurately. It was another year before it was ready for launch. In their typically frugal style, they loaded the spy satellite with film, launched it to take pictures, commanded it to land and then loaded it again and sent it back into space, until the capsule was too damaged to be reused.

In June of 1961, Convair Astronautics became General Dynamics Astronautics. It was now a full-fledged corporation, held by the parent company. The reorganization demonstrated the importance of the missile business, but it was also the aftermath of a calamity. For a second time, the company had been nearly ruined by a passenger plane. The sleek Convair 880 jet airliner was the fastest in the business, and the eccentric Howard Hughes ordered 30 of them for his airline, TWA. When it transpired that he could not pay for them, Convair lost $425 million. In 1959, General Dynamics was rescued by a new investor, and a couple years later they gave up on airliners.

The company's attention was focused on the Mercury flights. The Atlas D was a machine of daunting complexity, and out of 135 launched, 32 failed. These were sobering figures, and Astronautics took the responsibility for pilot safety very seriously. A man-rated Atlas was built at greater expense, more slowly and with more extensive testing than the ICBM models.[404] The Mercury program continued with a few more unmanned tests and some Mercury-Redstone suborbital flights, until they were confident that it was safe to orbit a man.

---

[404] Powell, Joel W., "The Mighty Atlas Part 10," *Spaceflight*, 55(5), May 2013.

On November 29, 1961, Atlas 93D put an ape named Enos into orbit. During the mission, he performed psychomotor tests involving colored lights and levers, getting a banana pellet when he did them correctly and a mild shock in his foot when wrong. But a malfunction in the experiment caused him to get a shock regardless of his choice, and in his frustration, he tore biomedical sensors off his body and yanked out his urinary catheter. The mission plan called for three orbits, but an overheating spacecraft and failure of a roll-stabilization jet led to the decision to land after two. Three hours after take-off, the spacecraft splashed down a few hundred miles south of Bermuda. When the capsule was recovered and opened, they found one very hot and angry chimpanzee inside.[405]

NASA hoped to put a man in space the same year as Gagarin, and their first attempt was scheduled for December 23. Atlas 109D had arrived at the Cape on November 30, but minor technical problems delayed the launch until February 20, 1962. On that morning, John Glenn was in the "Friendship 7" Mercury capsule, on Launchpad LC-14.

There was still skepticism about Charlie's ultra-light airframe. In Huntsville, one of von Braun's people said, "John Glenn is going to ride in that contraption? He should be getting a medal just for sitting on top of it before he takes off."[406]

Lift-off was 9:48 EST, engines boosting for five minutes before entering orbit. As the fuel was used up, the rocket became lighter and accelerated more rapidly, reaching a maximum of 7.7 g. Glenn was familiar with high g's from his training on the centrifuge, but he was surprised by the behavior of the ultra-light Atlas airframe as the liquid fuel emptied and the hull was maintained by gas pressure:

Just before the end of powered flight, there was one experience I was not expecting. At this time the fuel and lox tanks were getting empty and apparently the Atlas becomes considerably more flexible than when filled. I had the sensation of being out on the end of a springboard and could feel oscillating motions as if the nose of the launch vehicle were waving back and forth.[407]

When Glenn took off, he was cleared for seven orbits around the Earth, but once he was in space, a warning signal indicated a possible problem with the attachment of the heat shield. If it came loose during reentry, the capsule and its pilot would be incinerated, so NASA hoped the signal was a

[405] Kennedy, Gregory, "Mercury Primates," *History of Rocketry and Astronautics*, NASA, 1995.
[406] "Interview of Mr. K.J. Bossart by John L. Sloop," NASA, 1974.
[407] Glenn, John H. "Pilot's Flight Report," *Results of the First U.S. Manned Orbital Space Flight*, NASA, 1962.

malfunction. They decided to land on his third orbit, and as it approached the coast of California, the retro rockets were fired. Three engines produced a thousand pounds of thrust for a little over 10 seconds, enough impulse to slow the capsule by 500 ft/second.

The spacecraft was already in a very low orbit, and this small change in speed was enough to bring its orbit down and graze the atmosphere. Glenn was again subjected to 7.7 g's, in a fiery deceleration from 17,500 miles per hour to several hundred mph in six minutes. The capsule splashed down safely near Grand Turk Island, and a few hours later, the 3.5 ton Atlas stage reentered the atmosphere over South Africa. A number of pieces of the rocket were recovered, and Glenn was later presented with a piece of the stainless steel hull, found on a farm in Cape Province.

The Atlas put three more astronauts into orbit. The last of the Mercury missions was on May 15, 1963. Gordon Cooper made 22 orbits, spending 34 hours in space. The two-man Gemini capsules were launched by the second generation of the Titan missile, which had twice the payload capacity. However, the Atlas was used in the Gemini program to launch Agena target vehicles. The Saturn family of rockets was specifically built for the Apollo program and lofted 10 times and eventually 100 times the payload of the Atlas. The Saturn rockets were used only for the Apollo program and then retired from service, but Atlas and Titan had much longer lifetimes as launch vehicles for space probes and satellites.

Project SCORE rocket, Atlas-10B (*U.S. Air Force*).

Dora congradulates Charlie on SCORE satellite (*Courtesy of Scott Family*).

Collapse of depressurized Atlas-190D (*U.S. Air Force*).

Atlas Centaur carrying Pioneer-10 (*NASA*).

Charlie's analysis of interplanetary launch from orbit (*Courtesy of Bossart Family*).

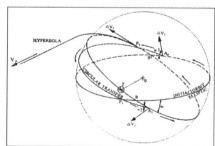

7

The Last Theorem

In his country of birth, Charlie was celebrated as "Mister Atlas." After the launch of the SCORE satellite in 1958, there was a flurry of articles about him in the Belgian press. His Aunt Vire was frequently interviewed for stories about his youth.[408]

Early in 1962, the Flemish television channel sent its reporter Jerome Verhaeghe to America with a film crew, to cover the launch of John Glenn.[409] Verhaeghe hosted a popular TV series about science called *Verover de Aarde* (Conquer the Earth). They toured Cape Canaveral and Cocoa Beach, and interviewed Byron MacNabb. Then the reporter headed to San Diego to film at General Dynamics and the Atlas test stands. Charlie and Verhaeghe joked about Belgian missiles called *Vogelpik*, a popular dart-throwing game. Getting more serious, the reporter asked, "How does it feel, as an expert, that these rockets are used as weapons of destruction?" He replied:

Well, I design rockets, but I hope they will never be used as weapons. As you know very well, there are different uses for rockets, such as space flight. I hope my work will contribute to the sciences and astronautics.[410]

On July 7, 1962, Charlie was knighted by King Boudewijn. The Belgian Consul General on the West Coast informed him of the honor. Specifically,

---

[408] The Bossarts' relatives in Belgium shared numerous newspaper clippings from the 1950s and 1960s, but often without an indication of the name of the paper or the exact date.

[409] Jerome Verhaeghe, "Ruimtevaart," *Verover de Aarde*, VRT, February 21, 1962.

[410] *Wel, Ik maak raketten.* But *ik hope, dat zij nooit zullen gebruikt worden als wapens. Zoals U wel weet... Er is een ander gebruik voor raketten. Dat is de ruimtevaart. Ik hoop dat mijn werk voornamelijk zal bijdragen tot de wetenschappen of ruimtevaart.*

he had been made an Officer in the Order of Leopold, the oldest and most prestigious award in Belgium, established by the nation's first king in 1832.

In 1963, Charlie was invited by the king to visit Belgium.[411] He and Connie arrived at the Brussels airport on October 19, where they were met by his cousin Daisy Dent, her husband Karel Vroom and his childhood best friend Jan Van Overloop.[412] After interviews with reporters, the Bossarts retired to Kalmthout, where they stayed at De Kievit with Daisy's family and her mother, Charlie's Aunt Vire. Charlie's boyhood home had been rented out after his father's death, and his mother had spent the last years of her life at her sister's hotel.

Aunt Vire suffered from diabetes and was not well enough to meet them at the airport. Uncle Russell had passed away just two weeks before, so Charlie was welcomed company at a sad time. Vire had followed Charlie's career with pride, amassing a large collection of newspaper and magazine clippings about his achievements. Although Charlie had a busy official schedule over the next two weeks, in his free time, he relaxed with his friends and relatives and went for long walks in the places where he had played as a boy and studied the local flora with his father.

The day after his arrival was a Sunday, and Charlie slept late, recovering from the long trip and the time zone change. He was still in his pajamas when a French journalist from *Le Matin* showed up at the door. The journalist and his photographer had spent most of the day driving around the quiet suburb, asking where the Bossarts were staying. But Daisy and her husband stood in the doorway and would not let them in. They assured them that Charlie needed his rest and was enjoying the good Belgian home cooking 'after years of inferior American food.' And that was all the reporter got for his exclusive story.[413]

On Monday, the Bossarts returned to Brussels for a busy day of official events. Charlie and Connie met with the U.S. Ambassador to Belgium, Douglas MacArthur II (nephew of the famous general). Following that, the Bossarts and Jan Van Overloop met with the Belgian Prime Minister, Théo Lefèvre.[414]

---

[411] *Visite de M. L'Ingenieur Karel J. Bossart et de Mma Bossart en Belgique,* Institut Belge d'Information ed de Documentation.

[412] "Aan Komst Atlasraket Brussel," newsreel footage from Flemish Television (VRT), October 19, 1963.

[413] "Une interview exclusive que n'en est pas une… M. Atlas-Bossart en pyjama," *Le Matin,* October 21, 1963.

[414] De Bruyn, F., "De Klap op de Vuurpijl," *Historische Verhalen,* No. 10, 1964.; "Vader van Atlasraket op Antwerps stadhuis," newspaper clipping of unknown origin, from Vire Dent's collection.; Press photos in the Bossart family collection.; "Bezoek Karel-Jan Bossart," newsreel footage from Flemish Television (VRT), October 21, 1963.

That afternoon, Charlie visited the Free University of Brussels, where he got his original mining engineering degree. He was greeted by the president of the university, Dr. Félix Leblanc, and introduced by the Chairman of the Belgian National Council for Science Policy, Dr. Lucien Massart. He received a school cap as a gift, and immediately put it on, to the applause of the students. In his talk, he predicted that men would travel to Venus and Mars by 1975, which was typical optimism in those days (maybe possible if massive spending had continued after the Apollo landings).

At a press conference held with Dr. Massart, he was asked questions about international cooperation in space and in particular cooperation between the two leading nations in space exploration, the United States and the Soviet Union. He believed it was possible and desirable, as long as military secrets were safeguarded. But there were plenty of new scientific discoveries waiting to be made in space, "As we say in America, the pie is big enough for everyone to get his slice."

Someone asked what it was like to be a tourist in the country of his birth. Charlie chuckled and replied, "One thing I've noticed is that the Flemish language is being spoken better. It's been purified." That would have made his father smile. The strong Flemish identity in modern Belgium had made the old Antwerp dialect, peppered with French words, very much out of fashion. Louis Bossart had worked hard to teach Charlie not to speak like that, and now everyone spoke proper Flemish.

The next couple days, Charlie and Connie were given tours of some technology companies, and they visited the aerodynamics research center in Rhode-St.-Genese, where he had worked after graduating from MIT.

On Thursday, he and his wife had an audience at the royal palace with the young and somewhat reclusive king of Belgium. There was controversy over whether his visit would be covered by the French or the Flemish television channels, an example of the tension between the two linguistic communities.[415] King Boudewijn was only the fifth king of the relatively young nation, but the Belgian monarchy already had a checkered history. His great grandfather, Leopold II, was infamous for torture and mass murder practiced on his rubber plantations in the Congo.[416] On the other hand, his grandfather, King Albert, was a national hero for his courageous actions in the First World War. He had defied the Germans and fought side by side with his fellow countrymen in Antwerp and at the battle of Yser. His wife, Queen Elisabeth, served as a nurse on the front lines. The next

---

[415] Newell Bossart, *Personal Communications*, October 25, 2014.
[416] *White King, Red Rubber, Black Death,* BBC documentary, February 24, 2004.

king, Leopold III, was a very different story. His rapid surrender to Hitler in 1940 was so unpopular that the royal family had to live in exile in Switzerland after the war. His return to Belgium in 1950 triggered violent protests and strikes, until he finally abdicated. His son, Boudewijn became King at the age of 20. He and his wife, Queen Fabiola, were somewhat mysterious figures, avoiding the typical high-profile life of European royalty.[417]

The next Monday, October 28, Charlie met again with his friend Jerome Verhaeghe, from the Flemish Radio and Television Channel.[418] He began the interview wearing his prized ULB student cap. When the reporter had visited the Bossart home the year before, he noticed a copy of Pieter Bruegel's painting of Dutch Proverbs. The 16th-century work depicts over a hundred folk sayings. Charlie had explained all of them to his boys, but he spared Connie some of the more off-color sayings.

Verhaeghe and Charlie both spoke Flemish during the interview, but after decades of not speaking Flemish, Charlie's speech was peppered with English words. At one point he referred to "my wife" and quickly corrected himself, saying "mijn vrouw." The word "wife" sounds like the Flemish word "wijf," which comes from the same Germanic language roots; but in Dutch culture, it is a very rude term for women. Afterwards, his relatives teased him for making the slip of the tongue.[419]

The next day, their official business was in Antwerp. In the morning, they met with The Royal Society of Flemish Engineers. Charlie was flattered when the chairman Dr. Daniel Vanderpitte compared him to the famous Belgian chemist Leo Baekeland, who invented Bakelite, the world's first plastic.

Later that morning, Charlie and his wife met with the mayor of Antwerp, Lode Craeybeckx, and he was declared an honorary citizen (*ereburger*) of the city. Craeybeckx, a socialist and Flemish nationalist, had been mayor since the end of the war. After the First World War, he had done time in prison for his involvement in a radical Flemish movement that had collaborated with the Germans, but he did not make the same mistake with the Nazis. In the Leys Room of Antwerp's city hall, the mayor gave a short speech, partly in English for the benefit of Connie. He praised Charlie for going to America, not just to make a fortune, but to rise in the world as a man of science.[420]

---

[417] A few years later, Charlie's son Newell named their family dog Boudewijn. They meant no disrespect, but when their cousin Daisy came to visit from Antwerp, she and her family were not very amused to find a yellow Labrador Retriever named after their king.
[418] "Fabriek Atlasraket San Diego," newsreel from Flemish Television (VRT), October 28, 1963.
[419] His South African relatives still tell this story and chuckle.

After the mayor, Charlie spoke briefly. Recalling his embarrassing gaffe on Flemish television the day before, he began by saying, "I will take a small risk and speak to you in Dutch."[421] He continued, "Here in City Hall, next to the river Scheldt and under the tower of Our Lady Cathedral, I feel at home." Speaking in distinctive Antwerp dialect, he referred to himself as *Sinjoor*, a slang term for residents of Antwerp. It was a corruption of *señor*, from centuries earlier, when the city was part of the Spanish Netherlands. After the speeches, everyone retired to a Flandria cruise ship, for a luncheon on the river.

Back in Kalmthout, the journalist Walter Geens had better luck than the French reporter meeting with The Father of the Atlas.[422] After a busy day, Charlie had changed from his suit into casual attire, donning a colorful wool cowboy shirt. The two men went for a walk in the heath just before sunset. Standing on a sand dune, they could see the moon in the sky, and the reporter asked when men might be sent there:

"Will we live to see it?"

"Of course," Charlie said, "First we have to solve problems such as how to purify the air we breathe and how to recycle the water that the astronauts use. But I think we will be ready for a trip to the Moon in 1969."

"And if you could participate, would you go?"

"Oh no, not me. I would much rather see the Moon from the Earth."

"And yet, you are constantly busy with the development of space travel. What is the appeal?" asked the reporter.

"The challenge," Charlie replied. "When we came up with plans for the Atlas rocket, there was hardly anyone who believed it could be created. But we proved that it could be done. Something like that makes a man very happy. Now we have even bigger plans. Progress never stops."

"Are these vehicles not a danger to the peace?" Geens asked.

"In the beginning, yes, when America needed the same weapons as Russia, we needed a certain balance. But that is the past. We do not work on new things for war. There has to be other things to do."

"Then what is the ultimate goal of space travel? Do you think human life will be better?"

"That depends on what you mean by a better life. If you mean better radios, better television sets, better devices of all kinds, then yes. The study of space will definitely provide a better material life. But a good part of my

---

[420] "Vader van Atlas-raket op Antwerps stadhuis" (Father of Atlas rocket at Antwerp City Hall). Like many of the family's newspaper clippings, the name of the Flemish paper is unknown.
[421] Flemish is a dialect of Dutch.
[422] De Bruyn, F., "De Klap op de Vuurpijl," *Historische Verhalen*, No. 10, 1964.

life does not depend on material things. Money is not everything. And viewed that way, space will not have much to give."

Charlie believed that investment in space technology would be paid back many times, but he did not share popular romantic dreams of man in space. He made his views clear at a panel discussion at the 1958 fall meeting of the American Rocket Society in Detroit.[423] Charlie was excited about the engineering challenges of space vehicles, and he believed man would learn from the scientific exploration of the solar system and important new technology that would be invented as a byproduct of astronautics. But he was skeptical about ideas like colonizing the Moon, which he did not believe was economically viable. He estimated that minerals mined on the Moon would cost $1,500 a pound. "The money could be better spent developing thermonuclear energy to make livable garden spots out of our arid wastelands in the Southwest," he said.

Back at home in America, Charlie's technical accomplishments were recognized in military and scientific circles. His awards included the Air Force Exceptional Civilian Award and the Medal of the American Ordnance Association (1958), the Sylvanus Albert Reed Award of the Institute of Aerospace Sciences and the James H. Wyld Memorial Award of the American Rocket Society (1959), The Robert H. Goddard Memorial Trophy and the Collier Trophy (awarded to Convair for the Atlas) in 1960, and the Bronze Space Achievement Medal of the British Interplanetary Society in 1962.

His family was grown up by the early 1960s. Newell graduated from Colorado College and served as a Naval Lieutenant (LTJG) on Swift Boat PCF-35, deployed in Cat Lo, Vietnam. Jan had earned a medical degree and served as a Lt. Commander on an aircraft carrier off the coast of Vietnam. Marion graduated from UCLA and worked in VISTA. Charlie was very proud of the service all his children performed.

On August 3, 1967, Charlie officially retired. Three hundred people attended a dinner held at the Hanalei Hotel, to honor him. Films of MX-774 launches were played, dozens of funny stories were told about mishaps and adventures during their work on the Atlas, and Congressman Bob Wilson flew out from Washington to speak. As father of the Atlas, he told the audience, Charlie is grandfather of the U.S. space program, and will soon be great-grandfather of the Man on the Moon. The Chairman of General Dynamics wrote to him:

[423] Pearson, Jean, "Space Exploration A Pipe Dream, Rocket Panel Told," *Detroit Free Press,* September 17, 1958.

Your faith in a revolutionary concept, your tenacity in achieving a critical national goal, the excellence of your technical leadership, your dedication in times of stress, and your quiet confidence were instrumental in creating the U.S. Air Force Atlas, which served as a vital element in our country's defense, first lofted free man around the globe, and led us to the stars.

In a letter to Dora, Charlie joked, "being fundamentally lazy, I don't find the adjustment to retired life difficult at all!" He and his wife went for swims in the ocean every day. He and his long-time friend Bill Dieter spent a couple weeks fishing in Alaska.

Ever since Dora had moved to South Africa, Charlie and Connie wanted to visit her, but they did not get the opportunity until after his retirement. In 1968, they finally made the journey to Africa, but not in a blimp, as Charlie once described in stories for his children.

The Pan American African route began with a seven-hour flight from New York to Dakar, where the Bossarts stayed for a day to rest and sightsee. Charlie must have recalled the days when Pan Am got its start flying the Sikorsky seaplanes that he had helped develop. When the airline first started service to Africa in 1941, they flew Boeing Clipper seaplanes in a series of short flights from New York to Bermuda, Azores, Lisbon and Dakar, which took a grueling 60 hours. In the summer of 1955, the airline began direct service from New York to Dakar, using Douglas DC-7B modified with additional fuel tanks.

From Dakar, the route made a series of hops down the west coast of Africa, to Monrovia, Accra, Kinshasa and finally Johannesburg, South Africa. Dora and her family met them in Johannesburg and brought them home. Since the mid-1950s, the Scotts lived in Bloemfontein, the regional capital of the Orange Free State of South Africa.

Like her father, Dora and her husband Dr. Frederick Scott were actively involved in the modern art scene.[424] The South African sculptor Gerard de Leeuw travelled from Johannesburg to make a clay bust of Charlie. He sat for the artist several times, and when the clay model was finished, a bronze bust was cast by the lost-wax process.

Charlie spent a month with his sister. The Scott family showed them around the country, starting with a tour of the famous Kimberley diamond mines. In two days of driving the trails of Kruger National Park, the largest

[424] "Dora Scott: A Memorial Exhibition," *South African Art Times*, April, 2013.; Smith, Marleen, "Bfn-vrou se broer pionier in ruimtetuie," *Volksblad*, February 23, 2002.

game preserve in Africa, they got to see every variety of big animal. They drove the beautiful Garden Route on the southeastern coast, a magnificent stretch of land including tropical forests, beaches, waterfalls and first-class resorts. But more than anything, they enjoyed the parties that Dora and Frik gave, with their interesting friends.[425]

In mid-May, the Bossarts left South Africa, continuing their plan to travel around the world. After visiting the rift valley in Kenya, they flew to Bombay and visited Agra and Katmandu. The poverty of India was a shock to them. They watched a funeral ceremony burn a dead body on the Ganges River, while boys swam and played nearby. In June, they journeyed from Calcutta to Bangkok, where they took boat trips on the rivers, shopped at floating markets and visited temples with gold-plated Buddhas. They befriended a couple of tourists from Durban, who were also on their way to Hong Kong as their next stop. It was an interesting opportunity to visit with South Africans of British descent. The next stop was the Golden Palace Hotel, in Hong Kong, where they witnessed Maoist protests against the "British Empire."

The final stop was Japan. Charlie and Connie spent a week touring southern Honshu (the main island), stopping at Osaka, Kyoto, Nara, and Takamatsu. A second week was spent just seeing the sights of Tokyo. The language barrier was more of a problem in Japan than anywhere else they had visited. It was difficult to strike out and explore on their own, as they preferred to do, so they ended up taking conducted tours. Serving girls cooked meals in their hotel room, and one evening they were having difficulty communicating what they wanted for dinner. Finally, Charlie stood up and did an imitation of a chicken, clucking and flapping his arms. When the surprised girl left to get cooking supplies, Charlie laughed, "I hope we don't get eggs!"

Back in San Diego, he resumed his favorite pastimes, such as sailing and swimming. From his hill-top home on Aranda Avenue, he had a beautiful view of the ocean and enjoyed watching the gray whale migrations in the fall. It was only a short walk down to the beach.

While Charlie enjoyed his retirement, General Dynamics Astronautics asked him to come in once a week and consult on various projects. His technical creativity and judgment was greatly valued. Among the projects he worked on was the Space Shuttle.

Late in 1968, NASA issued a request for proposals for space shuttle designs. This was a reusable launch vehicle that could go into orbit, and

---

[425] Their trip is detailed in letters and postcards to their children and to Dora.

reenter the atmosphere and glide to a landing.[426] Five companies, including General Dynamics, produced preliminary designs. General Dynamics' first proposal was unusual, using three similar manned stages, powered by LOX and LH2. Joined together at take-off, two of the stages would act as boosters but could be piloted back to the ground for a landing. The third would be the actual orbital shuttle, which would return to land after the orbital mission was completed.

In 1970, a second phase of proposals was invited. This time, General Dynamics partnered with North American Rockwell. The latter designed the orbiting shuttle, which rode on top of a General Dynamics manned booster.[427] The booster was to be powered by 12 large LOX/LH2 engines. These proposals were not accepted for the final shuttle contracts, which were awarded to Lockheed and Boeing.

Charlie also tinkered with ideas on his own time. One problem that especially intrigued him was bringing ice from the Arctic to supply California with fresh water. He did extensive structural analysis of a submarine icebreaker, that he called SLED.[428] His plan was to cut arctic sea ice into large bergs using a vertical icebreaking blade that extended from the top of a submerged craft. Looking something like the dorsal fin of a killer whale, the blade would penetrate the ice layer from below and cut through it as the submarine moved forward. Once carved off, the berg would be wrapped in plastic and towed south, where it would melt and the water could be pumped out.

Charlie had a life-long interest in math challenges, and in the early 1970s, he was a frequent contributor of solutions to the "Puzzle Corner" of MIT's magazine *Technology Review*.[429] One problem, from 1971, exemplified Charlie's problem-solving style. A reader suggested that a regular icosahedron and a regular dodecahedron of equal volumes would contain inscribed spheres of the same size. Charlie shows this was incorrect. First, he presented an intuitive argument: the 20-sided solid should be a better approximation to a sphere than the 12-sided one. Then he proved it rigorously by deriving the algebraic formulae for the volumes of the two

[426] Jenkins, Dennis R., "Broken in Midstride: Space Shuttle as a Launch Vehicle," *To Reach the High Frontier*, University of Kentucky Press, 2002.
[427] *Space Shuttle Aluminum Booster Study*, October, 1970.
[428] Bossart, *Strength of SLED Blade in the Icebreaker Mode*, Unpublished Notes, March 31, 1971.; Bossart, *Turning Maneuver of SLED*, Unpublished Notes, March 24, 1971.; Hawthorne, W.R., "The Early Development of the Dracone Flexible Barge," The Institution of Mechanical Engineers, London, 1961.
[429] "Puzzle Corner," *Technology Review*, October 1971, October 1972, February 1973.

polyhedrons. A good scientist often thinks this way; intuition gives a quick answer, and then careful logic, math or experimentation checks to be sure.

Number theory was one of Charlie's favorite math hobbies. This subject was concerned with the properties of integer numbers, such as how numbers are factored into primes. It seems to be a deceptively simple topic, where questions sometimes opened up whole new areas of mathematics. The most subtle type of problem in number theory was the search for integer solutions to equations. Basic algebra finds the roots of an equation, but they can be any real number, including irrational numbers. The additional constraint that the roots must be integers was beyond the capability of algebra. This is called the problem of Diophantine equations.

Charlie was fascinated by the most famous unsolved problem in mathematics: Fermat's Last Theorem. Pierre de Fermat was a brilliant French mathematician, living in the 17th century. He was one of the pioneers of number theory, a founder of the theory of probability, and he created a precursor to calculus before Newton.

The unsolved problem emerged from an old idea. Since ancient times, it was known that the lengths of the sides of a right triangle obeyed a simple law: the square of the hypotenuse is equal to the sum of the squares of the other two sides. In other words, if Z is the length of the hypotenuse, and X and Y are the lengths of the other two sides, right triangles obey the equation: $X^2 + Y^2 = Z^2$.

Furthermore it was known that there were "Pythagorean triples" of integer numbers that obeyed this relationship. For example, $3^2 + 4^2 = 5^2$ (i.e., $9 + 16 = 25$). As early as 3000 BC, Egyptian surveyors and architects used this fact to make right angles, by stretching ropes into a triangle of these proportions. Sometime in the 1630s, Fermat was reading about Pythagorean triples in a 3rd-century text on algebra, and he scrawled in the margins:

> *It is impossible for a cube to be the sum of two cubes, a fourth power to be the sum of two fourth powers, or in general for any number that is a power greater than the second to be the sum of two like powers. I have discovered a truly marvelous demonstration of this proposition that this margin is too narrow to contain.*

In other words, Fermat claimed to have proved that there were no integer triples that solved $X^3 + Y^3 = Z^3$ or $X^4 + Y^4 = Z^4$ or with any exponent higher than 2. For $X^3 + Y^3 = Z^3$, there are solutions such as 3, 4, $\sqrt[3]{91}$, but they are not all integer numbers (the cube root of 91 is approximately

4.4979). Fermat typically stated important theorems without proof, and in subsequent years, other mathematicians proved that he was usually (but not always) correct. The comment about sums of powers was discovered by Fermat's son, after his death, and mathematicians began what at first they thought would be the routine task of proving or disproving Fermat's last theorem.

But centuries passed. Resisting attack by some of the greatest minds of mathematics,[430] the theorem became a legendary problem; and substantial cash prizes were established for whoever could solve the puzzle. Many false proofs were presented and invalidated, and special cases were proved. Euler proved the case of power 3, Fermat himself proved the case for 4, Lagrange proved it for 5. By 1941, it was known that the theorem was true for all exponents smaller than 253,747,889, but the general theorem was unproved.

Charlie tinkered with Fermat's Last Theorem, off and on, for almost twenty years. In early 1957, when he took his two boys on a vacation to Hawaii, he brought a ream of paper, intending to work intensely on the problem. While his sons swam and surfed, he sat on the beach making notes and calculations. But after a few days, he thought better of this plan and threw the paper away, so he could focus on having a vacation with his children.[431]

Charlie applied classical number theory techniques such as Fermat would have used. On February 17, 1972, he had a nine-page proof officially notarized. Could his proof be correct? The mathematician Dr. Jeffrey Lagarias generously took the time to check the proof.[432] He wrote:

The attempted proof consists of ten lemmas and theorems, of which Theorem 10 is the final result. The method is an interesting approach, and the argument is written clearly. There appears however to be a slip in the proof, with the result that Lemma 8 is false. This invalidates the conclusion. I do not know if there is any way to salvage something from the argument.

The slip in the proof was subtle, but Dr. Lagarias followed with a counter example that proved Lemma 8 was false. So alas, Charlie's proof was very clever but not correct.

In 1995, the mathematician Andrew Wiles published the first successful proof of Fermat's Last Theorem. It was based on sophisticated modern

---

[430] Weisstein, Eric W. "Fermat's Last Theorem.," *www.mathworld.wolfram.com.*

[431] Karel Jan Bossart Jr., *Personal Communications,* November 9, 2015.

[432] Lagarias, Jeffry C., *Comment on Fermat Last Theorem Manuscript of Charlie Bossart,* University of Michigan, Ann Arbor, November 10, 2015.

mathematics that men of Fermat's day could hardly have imagined. Underlying his proof were deep connections between the theory of integer numbers and the theory of topology (geometrical shapes). The actual theorem of Fermat is not especially useful or important, except as a famous puzzle. The real treasure has been the new mathematics invented to tackle it.

In April of 1974, the author John Sloop visited Charlie at his home and found him in good spirits, discussing the history of Atlas and Centaur and Charlie's early career. In the fall, Charlie was invited to speak at the 25th Symposium of the International Astronautical Congress, which would meet in Amsterdam. He prepared the talk, but it was never given.

In the early 1970s, Charlie's doctor noticed a slight problem.[433] One of the routine tests was measuring the hematocrit, the percentage of packed red cells when a vial of blood is centrifuged. The normal range is 38-52. But by 1971, Charlie's red-cell count had fallen to 35. The next year it dropped to 30.

His son Jan was a doctor in San Francisco, and in November of 1972, he insisted that his father get to the bottom of the mysterious anemia. By then, his hematocrit was 22 and he was feeling fatigued and had little appetite. After running a battery of tests at the La Jolla Scripts Clinic, everything appeared normal except the unexplained low red-cell count. They tried more sophisticated tests, such as radioactive chromium to measure hidden internal bleeding, but none was discovered.

Charlie and Connie called their son for advice, and he arranged an appointment with a hematologist in San Francisco. They considered doing a transfusion, but just as mysteriously as it had fallen, his blood count rose to 28 and he felt much better. Looking back at his medical records, they saw that a slow decline in his count had begun as far back as 1962, but it had not been a cause for concern then. Even the specialist was baffled, ruling out cancer or any hereditary condition, he could offer no diagnosis. They checked his bone marrow, but found paradoxically that he was "making red blood cells like mad."[434] The hematologist advised Charlie to eat iron-rich foods.

In the meantime, his doctor in La Jolla continued to research the literature and came across an extremely rare blood condition called paroxysmal nocturnal hemoglobinuria (PNH). Only a few people out of a

[433] Dr. Karel Jan Bossart Jr., *personal communication*, August, 2014.; Letter to Dora from Connie, March 22, 1973.
[434] Bossart, Charlie, Letter to Newell, January 17, 1973.

million developed this disease, and it typically went undiagnosed for years, since few doctors ever saw a case. There was a specific diagnosis: the Ham test. A sample of blood was placed in a mild acid, which would cause afflicted red cells to rupture and disintegrate, and Charlie tested positive. Finally he had his diagnosis, but unfortunately it was a serious and incurable disease.

First described in 1866, PNH has only recently been understood as an acquired genetic defect in the stem cells that generate the various types of blood cells. Each type of PNH blood cell malfunctions in some way as a result. Red cells burst and become depleted, white cells fight infection less efficiently; but the most dangerous problem was not the anemia, it was blood clotting caused by abnormal platelets.

In February of 1973, his condition suddenly worsened and Charlie suffered several blood clots. One in his abdomen required emergency surgery. His life was saved by Dr. Brent Eastman, a pioneering trauma surgeon who later became president of the American College of Surgeons. After the surgery, Dr. Eastman was impressed by how quickly Charlie recovered and healed. As always, Charlie was courageous and positive.

At the time that he was diagnosed, PNH was poorly understood, and the only treatments available simply addressed the harmful symptoms of the disease.[435] Doctors prescribed Coumadin, a powerful "blood-thinning" medication, to protect against clotting. Severe bouts of anemia were treated with transfusions. Although easily fatigued when his red-cell count dropped, Charlie remained sharp and was able to continue working on his mathematical hobbies and technical problems.

The anticoagulation therapy extended Charlie's life for several years, but prolonged blood-thinning treatment had its own risks of bleeding. Ultimately the treatment itself caused his death. On August 3, 1975, he suffered a massive hemorrhage in his stomach and passed away peacefully in his home later that day.

Memorial services were held two days later at the La Jolla Presbyterian Church. At the service, Congressman Bob Wilson said, "Charlie Bossart is to space what the Wright brothers were to aviation." The pastor, Dr. Harry Brahams, concluded his eulogy with, "His son said it best...and I think it would even be appropriate to say it here in this Sanctuary...he was a hell of a man!" According to Charlie's wishes, his body was cremated by the Telophase Society. He was survived by three children and six grandchildren.

---

[435] An effective treatment was not discovered until 2007, a drug called Soliris, which blocks the specific antibiotic substance from the complement system that attacks PNH cells.

Connie later moved to San Francisco to live near her son Jan and her sister Katharine. She passed away in 1999, at the age of 92.

In 1988, Newell and Myrle Ann Bossart and their two boys visited Kalmthout, while they were on a tour of Europe. They got to know Charlie's cousin Daisy and her family (Aunt Vire, Daisy's mother, had passed away in 1966). They got a tour of local historical sites and went for a walk on the heath, where Newell's father spent so much time exploring as a boy. The people who lived in the former Bossart home were kind enough to let them visit and tour the house. Remembering the stories about their grandfather during the war, the boys imagined that there might still be gold coins hidden in the walls of the basement.

In 2000, they visited their Aunt Dora Scott in South Africa and met their cousins Willem, Louis and Frederick. The Scotts were a dynamic force in the local art community, and formed the Bloemfontein Group, which met at their home for the first few years. By 1966, the Group had achieved national prominence with a major exhibition at the South African National Gallery in Cape Town. Dr. Scott passed away in 1976, and Dora carried on the activity. In 1985, enough money was gathered to open a local museum, and the Scott family donated 24 art works to the project.[436]

Dora enjoyed remarkable health and longevity, living independently in the family home until the last weeks of her life. She never lost her sense of humor. When the intensive-care nurse brought her some juice, she raised the glass saying, "santé" (an French toast). At the age of 99, Dora Bossart Scott passed away peacefully on the afternoon of February 24, 2013. In Kalmthout, just two days later, Charlie's cousin Daisy died.

The Atlas rocket was a legacy that lived on after Charlie. In the Atlas II, the stainless steel balloon tank was extended 9 feet longer than the Atlas I space rocket, and 19 feet longer than the tank of the original Atlas ICBM. The Atlas II was used for 63 missions, until 2004. That was the last main rocket stage based on Charlie's ultra-light pressure-stabilized design. The Atlas III and Atlas V (there is no Atlas IV) use some of Convair's systems, but Lockheed Martin owned the Astronautics division by that time, and the new Atlas airframes more closely resembled their Titan rocket. However, the stainless steel balloon still lives on in the Centaur stage, which is in active use to this day.

---

[436] Dora Scott Memorial Exhibition, March 27 to April 7 2013, Oliewenhuis Art Museum.

Charlie wearing a school beanie at
ULB and in 1963, Charlie meeting with
Belgian Prime Minister Lefevre (*Courtesy
of Vroom Family*).

In South Africa, Charlie, Dora, Belgian
scholar Herman Liebaers, Connie and
Frik Scott (*Courtesy of Scott Family*).

Charlie with Aunt Vire, Charlie helping
Jan with his homework (*Courtesy of
Vroom Family*).

A page from Charlie's proof of Fermat's
Last Theorem (*Courtesy of Bossart Family*).

Acknowledgements

"I still don't know why Americans write a lot about von Braun and nothing about their own designers such as Bossart." [437] I was getting a scolding from a Russian space historian, Sergei Andreev, whom I knew from my work on the history of the Soviet space program. It was the 100th anniversary of Wernher von Braun's birth, and I had been praising a recent biography of him.[438] Sergei had a strong belief that American and Russian rocket pioneers were neglected by historians, and the importance of captured German scientists was overemphasized.

I shared his view about historical bias, but I was guilty of knowing less than I should about Charlie Bossart. I knew him as the developer of America's Atlas missile, but I was disappointed to find only a few one-page articles about him on the internet. While many books have been written about the Atlas missile, there was no biography of its principal inventor. Furthermore, I discovered that Charlie's son, Newell and his family lived only a few miles from my home. This seemed like a good short project to do before I tackled the giant book that I had researched on Soviet planetary probes. Four years later, I am amused to think that I imagined this would be a short project.

Many people have helped in the research for this book. Karel Bossart's sons, Karel Jan Jr. and Newell, and Newell's wife Myrle Ann shared their recollections of people, events and family history. Newell's sons, Chase and Russell, shared information from interviews with their grandmother. Cornelia Bossart's niece, Cornelia Young, shared her knowledge of the history of the Chase family, as did her nieces, Virginia Umberger and Katharine Wolpe, and nephew, George Baum.

In South Africa, Karel's sister, Dora, helped. I had only a few indirect communications with her, but she told many stories to her children, made

---

[437] Sergei Viktorovich Andreev, *Personal Communication*, March 24, 2012.
[438] Neufeld, Michael, *Von Braun: Dreamer of Space, Engineer of War*, Knopf, 2007.

some video interviews, was interviewed by Myrle Ann Bossart and wrote a long letter of recollections to Karel's granddaughter Mary Bossart Halfpenny. Her three sons and their families supplied a wealth of information, letters, newspaper clippings, and photographs. They are: Willem, Isabel and their daughter Dora; Louis and Leenta; and Frederick and Susan. Jan Vroom, the son of Daisy Dent, located a number of letters from Karel to his parents in Antwerp; and he was assisted by Willem's daughter Dora. Karel Bossart's granddaughter, Mary Bossart Halfpenny, supplied me with a biography she wrote as a student.

Thanks to the family of Gerard De Leeuw for kindly granting permission to use a photograph of his sculpture of Karel Bossart. The artists Cat Leonard and James Mahoney helped me greatly with the book cover design.

In Belgium, I'd like to thank Saskia De Schepper in the municipal school system of Antwerp, Walter Resseler of the Royal Society for Nature and Clean Cities (KVNS), and José Cleeremans at the Ministry of Foreign Affairs. I want to thank Karen Nicolas for helping me translate letters in Flemish. Christelle Debeer of the von Kármán Institute sent me photographs from early Belgian aviation research. The professional genealogist, Alain Van Wayenberge, found helpful information about the Bossart and Tyck families. Tim De Canck at VRT television in Belgium helped to obtain video footage of Karel Bossart.

At the San Diego Air & Space Museum, I want to thank Alan Renga, Robert Bradley and Debbie Seracini. Allen Vinzant, who worked on the Atlas at Convair, kindly answered many questions. Thanks to Dan Shumaker for the use of his photograph of the Colgate-Larsen CL-15. Thanks also to Kay Peterson at the archives center of the Smithsonian Institution. John H. Hargenrader at the NASA History Program Office found the interviews with Karel Bossart and Krafft Ehricke done by John Sloop. Mary Ruwell and Kim van Lookeren Campagne, at the U.S. Air Force McDermott Library, searched the archives of George de Bothezat's papers. John Kelly, grandson of Bill Patterson, provided helpful information. Betty Boyle, the daughter of Bill Dieter, and her daughter Sarah Christine kindly provided photographs and information. Alan Reddig told me some stories about the history of Fleetwings, where his father was an airplane designer. John Kyros helped me find information at the General Motors Heritage Center.

I had some helpful conversations with historians Stephen Johnson, Jacob Neufeld and Asif Siddiqi. Many thanks to Andrew Glassner and Mark

Lowery for reading my manuscript and providing feedback and suggestions on style.

Many improvements in this book resulted from the structural edit done by William Boggess at NY Book Editors. Special thanks to my sister in-law, Christine Mitchell, who did a detailed proofreading and made corrections to the manuscript.

The mathematician, Dr. Jeff Lagarias, generously took the time to check Charlie Bossart's lengthy proof of Fermat's Last Theorem. I asked him if I might hire one of his students to do this, and I was delighted when two days later, Jeff sent me a manuscript with his own analysis of the proof.

I have also benefited from those especially great examples of the history of technology. Michael Neufeld's recent book, *Von Braun*, was an excellent biography of a rocket designer. For history of science, there are outstanding works such as Donald Mackenzie's history of guidance systems, *Inventing Accuracy*; Asif Siddiqi's history of Soviet rocketry, *The Red Rockets' Glare*; and Stephen Johnson's histories of systems management, *The Secret of Apollo* and *The United States Air Force and the culture of innovation*.

A special thanks to the Russian space historian Sergei Viktorovich Andreev, who started me on this project with the exchange I described above. We discussed the idea of him translating this book into Russian, but sadly, he passed away in October of 2013. Sergei was a humorous fellow, and shared a lot of unwritten history (and gossip) about the Soviet space program.

Index

Rocketdyne Division of NAA, 106, 112, 114, 118, 119, 125, 130, 137, 152

Rockne Knute (TWA 599 Crash), 39

Roosevelt, Franklin D., 21, 57

Rosen, Milton, vii, 101, 146, 159, 162, 165

Rosenbaum, Mort, 139, 167

RTV-A-2 Test Rocket, 88, 89, 90, 93, 96, 97, 100, 102, 105, 111, 120

Ryan Airlines Incorporated, 24, 25, 95

S

Schriever, General Bernard, 122, 124, 127, 128, 132, 133, 134, 138, 152, 158, 160

SCORE Satellite Mission, 160, 161, 162, 163, 171, 177

Scott, Frederick (Frik), 56, 66, 184

SCR-584 Radar, 84, 85, 92, 101, 103, 140

Sergievsky, Boris Vasilievich, 44, 45, 46, 47

Service Technique de l'Aéronautique Belge (STAé), 27

Shick, Ralph, 69

Sikorsky S-29A, 21, 36, 45

Sikorsky S-35, 21, 22, 32

Sikorsky S-38, 33, 36, 38, 44

Sikorsky S-40, 33, 34, 36, 37, 38, 43, 44

Sikorsky S-42, 44

Sikorsky S-43, 44, 45, 51

Sikorsky, Igor Ivanovich, 20, 21, 31, 32, 33, 34, 36, 37, 38, 39, 40, 42, 43, 44, 45, 46, 50, 51, 57, 68, 79, 183

Sloop, John, 17, 27, 40, 46, 47, 50, 52, 104, 123, 125, 126, 128, 134, 137, 158, 165, 167, 168, 169, 170, 174, 188, 193

Snark Cruise Missile, 77, 82, 84, 95, 125, 140

Spencer, Percival, 51, 52, 55

Sputnik Satellite, 74, 96, 139, 145, 146, 147, 154, 158, 159, 160, 162, 163

Stainless Steel, 35, 47, 48, 49

Stalin, Joseph, 75, 112

Standley, Lloyd William, 78, 90, 98, 105

Starlite Motel, 141, 148, 172

Stern, Marvin, 127, 131, 132, 138, 139, 152

Sycamore Canyon Test Site, 137, 138, 150, 169

T

Taylor, Charles, 19

Teapot Committee, 124, 125, 126, 127, 154

Teller, Edward, 122, 123, 124, 125, 132

Thor Missile, 143, 163, 165

Titan Missile, 130, 133, 136, 154, 162, 175, 190

Trans World Airline (TWA), 32, 39, 40, 41, 173

Triatomic Hydrogen, 87

Truman, Harry S., 113

Tsiolkovsky, Konstantin Eduardovich, 26, 86, 87, 116, 129, 159, 167

Tukhachevsky, Mikhail Nikolayevich, 61, 75

Tyck, Carolina, 3, 6, 79, 81, 115

Tyck, Elvire Maria (Aunt Vire), 5, 14, 43, 65, 115, 146, 177, 178, 190

U

Université Libre de Bruxelles (ULB), 13, 14, 180

V

V-1 Cruise Missile, 56, 64, 65, 72, 82, 84, 85, 101

Made in the USA
San Bernardino, CA
27 December 2016